The Metabolism of

INSECTS

The Metabolism of
INSECTS

by

DARCY GILMOUR

*Division of Entomology, Commonwealth Scientific
and Industrial Research Organization, Canberra,
Australia*

OLIVER & BOYD
EDINBURGH AND LONDON

OLIVER AND BOYD LTD

Tweeddale Court
Edinburgh 1

39A Welbeck Street
London W.1

First published . . . 1965

© 1965, Darcy Gilmour

Printed in Great Britain
by Oliver and Boyd Ltd., Edinburgh

To the memory of
CONSETT DAVIS
whose encouragement of lesser colleagues
is not forgotten

Preface

The science of biochemistry has largely outgrown its analytical phase, in which the primary concern was to disintegrate the living mechanism and extract fragments in as pure a state as possible for critical examination. During this phase biochemists were gratified to learn that identical reactions could be recognized in material derived from organisms of widely separate relationships. Individual reactions first identified in organisms as disparate as bacteria, fungi, green plants and mammals were arranged in sequences which could be assumed with reasonable certainty to be valid for all. This approach was eminently successful and from it arose the concept of the unity of biochemistry: that the fundamental molecular transformations are the same in all cells. This concept, though perfectly valid at the level of individual reactions and some reaction sequences, is cold comfort to biologists, who know that a mouse is not a man. Now that biochemistry is providing more and more knowledge of the integration and control of cellular transformations the dilemma begins to be resolved, and biologists can hope for an understanding of the differences between organisms in terms of metabolism. For the individual reactions are but as the notes on a symphonic score; the same notes may be used many times, but the sound that emerges from a full orchestra is susceptible of infinite variation, just as is the total pattern of molecular transformations we call metabolism. Thus the principle of biochemical unity does not preclude us from inquiring into the metabolism of special groups of animals and since the insects have been studied more thoroughly than any other group outside the mammals there is a sufficient body of information on which to base an account of their metabolism. The insects, of course, are themselves a very diverse group, and in searching for a central theme I have had to make many generalizations, some of which will probably be shown by future work to have been unjustified.

Although the subject of this book is the total pattern of metabolism in the insects, it includes a considerable amount of detail of individual reactions, only a few of which are peculiar to insects, the majority being common to a wide range of organisms. Moreover, in dealing with aspects of metabolism which have been less thoroughly studied in insects I have indicated in brief outline the kinds of transformations which could be expected, by drawing on knowledge of similar processes in other animals. Not everyone will agree with this approach, and I probably risk the censure of insect biologists for including too much material which they would consider extraneous to the main theme, and of general biochemists for the terseness of some summaries of biochemical events. I believe, however, that this information is of fundamental value for an understanding of metabolism and that without it this book would not have been complete in itself, but would have had to be read in conjunction with a textbook of biochemistry. My aim throughout this work has been not so much a description of the fluxes in what I have called the total pattern, but an exploration of the mechanisms by which the pattern is determined and the underlying reasons for the changes.

I hope the book will be of value to students both of general biology and of biochemistry. For the benefit of the former, who might be deterred by biochemical detail, I have opened the discussion of each section of metabolism in general terms, aiming to lead the reader by easy stages into the study of the complex of interlocking reactions eventually uncovered. Moreover, I have summarized the multitude of molecular transformations as far as possible into charts which emphasize the flow of metabolism rather than individual details. Thus the student of zoology may concentrate on the main theme, taking for granted the details of biochemical reactions, although the information is there if he wishes to inquire more deeply into molecular mechanisms. Biochemists, I hope, may find it instructive to learn how the chemical changes which are the main subject matter of their science are organized into the special metabolic patterns of insects, which are so different from those of the mammals with which they are more familiar. I have assumed in the reader some basic knowledge of organic chemistry, but wherever possible I have provided aids to understanding in the form of structural formulae. These follow the normal conventions of chemical shorthand in the more complex molecules, indicating carbon atoms, along with the appropriate number of accompanying hydrogen atoms, by angles in either closed- or open-chain structures.

The literature on the metabolism of insects is now extensive, and the list of references at the end of this book represents a necessarily arbitrary selection. Wherever possible I have referred to review articles from which the reader may gain access to many original papers; other references have been drawn mostly from the more recent literature. I take this opportunity of apologizing to many authors whose findings I have used in the text but whose names do not appear among the references.

I am grateful to the Executive of the Commonwealth Scientific and Industrial Research Organization, who gave me permission to write the book, to several colleagues in the Division of Entomology, who read parts of the manuscript, and to Mr L. A. Marshall and Mrs G. Palmer, who prepared the figures.

Contents

1: Energy Metabolism

Part 1: Energy Production

Sources of Energy

Insects, like other animals, derive their energy from the food they eat. In the course of digestion, the food taken into the alimentary canal is broken down into units small enough to be absorbed through the gut wall and transported in the haemolymph to nourish all the cells of the body. Thus the large carbohydrate molecules are degraded to their unit sugars, and proteins to amino acids, while fats are either absorbed unchanged or broken down to fatty acids and glycerol. The relatively small molecules resulting from this digestion may be used immediately to provide energy for life, or, if they are absorbed in excess of energy needs, may be built up again into larger molecules in the synthesis of either new living substance or depots of food reserves.

Energy is released from organic molecules principally by oxidation. Biologically, such energy-yielding oxidations are accomplished by the removal of atoms of hydrogen (or electrons) from the substrate and their transfer to other acceptors within the cell. In aerobic organisms, electrons removed from the substrate are united eventually with oxygen, which with the absorption of protons from the environment, is thereby reduced to water, but in anaerobic organisms alternate acceptors are used. The complete combustion of the carbon skeleton of organic molecules within the cell involves also a number of decarboxylations, that is, the removal of the atoms of carbon dioxide from the substrate. The carbon dioxide produced in this way is released into the environment. The entry of oxygen into and the exit of carbon dioxide from an organism may be referred to as respiration, although this term is also extended to cover the whole course of biological oxidation. Since the relative amounts of carbon, hydrogen and oxygen vary in the different classes of organic molecules which are available as substrates for biological oxidation, the ratio of the volumes of carbon dioxide expired to oxygen inspired by an animal may give a clue to the source of energy. This ratio, the respiratory quotient (RQ), is 1·0 for carbohydrates (general formula $C_nH_{2n}O_n$), averages around 0·7 for fats (general formula, for saturated fatty acids, $C_nH_{2n}O_2$), and has a value somewhere between these two limits for proteins, in which the constituent amino acids have a wide variety of carbon skeletons. In animals, the most urgent demands for energy are made by the muscles, and the kind of substrate oxidized to provide this energy may conveniently be determined by measuring the respiratory quotient during exercise. It has been found that in the majority of animals the extra respiration of exercise has an RQ of 1·0, indicating that carbohydrate is the fuel for muscular activity. This preference for carbohydrate as an energy source has concentrated the attention of investigators on the catabolism of this class of organic molecule, so that the pathway for the oxidation of carbohydrate was the first to be worked out in detail and is still by far the best understood.

Insects are among the most successful of aerobic animals, and may expend energy during flight in amounts which are prodigous in relation to their body weight. They thus offer attractive subjects for the study of the energy sources of muscular activity. Such studies have revealed that a number of insects have an unusual ability to derive their energy for the muscular activity of flight from the oxidation of substrates other than carbohydrate. Members of several orders oxidize fat, either exclusively or principally, during flight. These orders include a number of insects which perform migratory flights of long duration, although the ability to oxidize fat is not confined to the migratory species. The desert locust, embarked on a flight of several hours' duration, burns mostly carbohydrate for a short time, but then switches over to the oxidation of fat, this change being reflected in a fall in the RQ. A similar sequence is found in the aphid, *Aphis fabae*. Butterflies also burn fat in flight—indeed the metabolism of their flight muscles may be obligatorily linked to the oxidation of this substrate. A butterfly feeding on nectar may have a resting RQ in excess of 1·0, suggesting the metabolic conversion of carbohydrate to fat. During flight, however, the RQ drops to 0·7, indicating that fat is being burned in the muscles, even though the crop, and presumably the blood, are well supplied with sugars. There is an obvious biological advantage in this ability to burn fats, especially for animals which perform long migratory flights, since fat, being more reduced than carbohydrate, yields more energy per unit weight on combustion—provided it is burned with the same efficiency as is carbohydrate. Migratory birds also consume quantities of fat on their long flights and their flight muscles, like those of migrating insects, are probably adapted to the combustion of fatty acids.

The flight muscles of other insects require different substrates. Many species, especially members of the Diptera, follow the familiar vertebrate pattern, exhibiting a respiratory quotient of 1·0 during exercise. In fact, the metabolism of the flight muscles of flies may be as tightly linked to the oxidation of carbohydrate as is that of butterflies to the oxidation of fat. The total duration of flight in *Drosophila* is closely related to the amount of its glycogen reserves. Once these reserves are exhausted the fly is quite incapable of flight, even though this species, like most insects, may have large reserves of depot fat in its body. A similar situation is found in the mosquito, *Culex*, but, once flown to exhaustion, *Culex* may be stimulated after a period of rest to fly again. Presumably the period of rest allows time for the mobilization of further reserves, perhaps by the conversion of fat to carbohydrate.

As a general rule, animals use protein or amino acids as a source of energy only under conditions of starvation, when no other fuel is available, but some insects run counter even to this rule. The free amino acids which are present in large amounts in the blood of all insects may constitute the mobile energy source in some species. The haemolymph of the blood-sucking tsetse fly, for instance, contains little or no carbohydrate, but is very rich in the amino acid proline, which serves as the fuel for flight, transferring its amino groups to other acceptors and yielding up its carbon skeleton for oxidation in the flight muscles.

The cellular pathways for the oxidation of carbohydrate, fat and amino acids are long and complex. They involve a multitude of steps in which energy is released in small amounts and trapped in a form usable by the living organism. The nucleotide adenosine triphosphate (ATP) has a central rôle in this conservation of energy. This compound is made up of the purine adenine, attached to the sugar ribose which carries three phosphate groups in ester linkage on its terminal carbon atom. The two terminal phosphates of ATP are relatively labile and can readily be split off by hydrolysis to yield adenosine diphosphate (ADP), then adenosine mono-phosphate (adenylic acid, AMP). These hydrolyses are exergonic reactions. The free energy which they release can be used by the living organism in a variety of ways, notably, for instance, in the performance of mechanical work by muscle. Conversely, the energy realized in the many small oxidative steps in the catabolism of foodstuffs is conserved in the cell by the simultaneous synthesis of ATP from ADP and inorganic phosphate. A majority of these small oxidative steps involves the removal of two atoms of hydrogen from the substrate molecule. Two coenzymes of wide-spread significance in biology are involved in these dehydrogena-tions. The first of these is nicotinamide-adenine dinucleotide (NAD), formerly known as co-zymase, coenzyme I, or diphospho-pyridine nucleotide (DPN); the second is nicotinamide-adenine dinucleotide phosphate (NADP), formerly known as coenzyme II, or triphosphopyridine nucleotide (TPN). Both compounds contain the vitamin nicotinamide, which insects are unable to synthesize for themselves and must obtain preformed in the diet. The nicotinamide is combined with ribose phosphate to form a nicotinamide nucleotide, which in turn is attached in a pyro-phosphate linkage to adenine nucleotide. In the second co-enzyme, the second carbon of the ribose portion of the adenine nucleotide carries a third phosphate group. These two coenzymes, by accepting two electrons from the substrate to be oxidized are converted to their reduced forms, which will be referred to as $NADH_2$ and $NADPH_2$. Although the removal of two electrons is the significant event from the point of view of oxido-reduction, it should also be mentioned, for the sake of completeness, that of the two protons simultaneously removed from the substrate, one is accepted by the coenzyme and the other, under normal conditions of pH, is removed to the environment. Of the two coenzymes, NAD is by far the more important in energy metabolism, the function of NADP being removed from the main stream of catabolism. Some of the dehydrogenations in which NAD acts as electron acceptor are linked with the simultaneous synthesis of ATP from ADP and inorganic phosphate; others are not. Energetically, the most important part of the oxidation process is the transfer of the two electrons from $NADH_2$ through the cytochromes, which are a series of haem-proteins of graded oxidation-reduction potentials, to oxygen. This process, which will be considered in detail later under the heading Terminal Oxidation, results in the synthesis of three molecules of ATP for each pair of electrons transferred, the overall result being the reduction of one atom of oxygen to water, and the oxidation of $NADH_2$ back to NAD.

After this brief summary of the general principles of biological oxidation, we may pass to a more detailed examination of the pathways and enzyme-catalysed reactions involved in this process in insects.

Catabolism of Carbohydrate

Although, as we have seen, carbohydrate may not be either a preferred or a possible substrate for energy production for some specific purposes in insects, it is still probably true to say that carbohydrate is the most readily available source of energy for the majority of insect cells, as it is for the generality of animal and plant cells, and certainly the enzymes involved in the catabolism of carbohydrate are to be found in many different tissues of a wide variety of insects. The complete pathway for the oxidation of glucose and related carbohydrates is shown in figure 1. The figure is divided into two parts, corresponding with the natural division in the cell between the soluble enzymes of the cytoplasm, which perform the reactions shown on the left hand page, and the solid, structurally-oriented system of enzymes and electron-carriers of the mitochondria, which perform the reactions shown on the right hand page.

The Embden-Meyerhof Pathway

The cytoplasmic enzymes carry out the linked series of re-actions, usually known as the Embden-Meyerhof sequence,[58],[24],[12] which results in the splitting of a molecule of glucose to form two molecules of pyruvic acid, the nett synthesis of two molecules of ATP, and the reduction of two molecules of NAD to $NADH_2$.

The initial step in this series is the phosphorylation of glucose to glucose-6-phosphate. Energy is needed for this synthesis, and so the phosphate is transferred from ATP by a transphosphorylation process catalysed by the enzyme hexokinase. The participation of ATP is also needed at a subsequent step, the phosphorylation of fructose-6-phosphate to fructose-1,6-diphosphate. Thus the energy stored in the terminal phosphate linkages of two molecules of ATP are needed to prime the catabolic process, before there can be any release of energy from oxidation. When the glucose polymer, glycogen, enters directly as a substrate into the Embden-Meyerhof sequence, ATP is not needed for the intial phosphorylation. Phosphate can enter directly into the cleavage of a glucose unit from glycogen catalysed by the enzyme phosphorylase; in other words, the energy stored in the glycosidic bond is preserved in the phosphate ester formed. The ester produced in the phosphorylase reaction is glucose-1-phosphate, which is readily converted to glucose-6-phosphate by the enzyme phosphoglucomutase.

Glycogen, which is the major substrate for the Embden-Meyerhof sequence in mammalian muscle, is stored in insect muscle and undoubtedly serves as the source of energy under some circumstances. However, the mobile energy source in many insects is the disaccharide trehalose, which must represent the starting point for carbohydrate catabolism in many cells. Trehalose is the physiologically important blood sugar of insects; its concentration is maintained by hormonal action, just as is the blood glucose of mammals. If blood trehalose is depleted, by the energy demands of muscle, for instance, it is reconstituted at the expense of glycogen stored in the fat body. Homogenates of dipteran muscle, in particular, have been shown to oxidize trehalose rapidly to carbon dioxide and water. As far as is known, the pathway for the catabolism of trehalose involves the participation of the hydrolytic enzyme trehalase, which splits trehalose to two molecules of glucose. It is not known whether insects also contain an enzyme capable of the phosphorylytic cleavage of trehalose. Such an enzyme, an analogue of which is known in the sucrose phosphorylase of yeast which splits sucrose in the presence of phosphate to yield glucose-1-phosphate and fructose, could be of advantage in that its participation would conserve one molecule of ATP for every molecule of trehalose entering the Embden-Meyerhof sequence.

The hexokinases of insects, like those of vertebrates, are capable of transferring phosphate from ATP to either glucose, fructose or mannose. Fructose-6-phosphate is on the direct pathway of carbohydrate catabolism (fig. 1), while mannose-6-phosphate is converted to fructose-6-phosphate by the enzyme phosphomannoisomerase. This enzyme apparently occurs in some insects which successfully metabolize mannose. It may be absent from others, however, and since mannose-6-phosphate may competitively inhibit some enzymes of the Embden-Meyerhof sequence, mannose can be harmful to these forms. The toxicity of mannose to the honeybee is believed to be the consequence of such a mechanism. In mammals, galactose also enters the Embden-Meyerhof sequence through a specific galactokinase, but this enzyme, although probably present in insects, has not been positively identified. Furthermore, pentose sugars may be catabolized by a mechanism which yields glyceraldehyde-3-phosphate by the transfer of a two-carbon fragment from a pentose-phosphate substrate to another sugar acting as acceptor. This reaction forms part of the pentose cycle, a metabolic pathway which seems not to be concerned primarily with energy production, and thus need not be considered in detail at this point (see Chapter 3). Since the pentose cycle provides a means for the interconversion of sugars of from three to seven carbon atoms, it is clear that its presence in cells, along with the reactions mentioned above, make possible the entry of most carbohydrates of metabolic importance into the Embden-Meyerhof sequence.

The sole oxidative step of the Embden-Meyerhof pathway is the dehydrogenation of phosphoglyceraldehyde to phosphoglyceric acid. The electron acceptor in this reaction is NAD. Removal of the dehydrogenated intermediate from the enzyme involves a phosphorylytic, rather than a hydrolytic process, so that the end products are 1,3-diphosphoglycerate and $NADH_2$. The diphosphate is capable of phosphorylating ADP to form

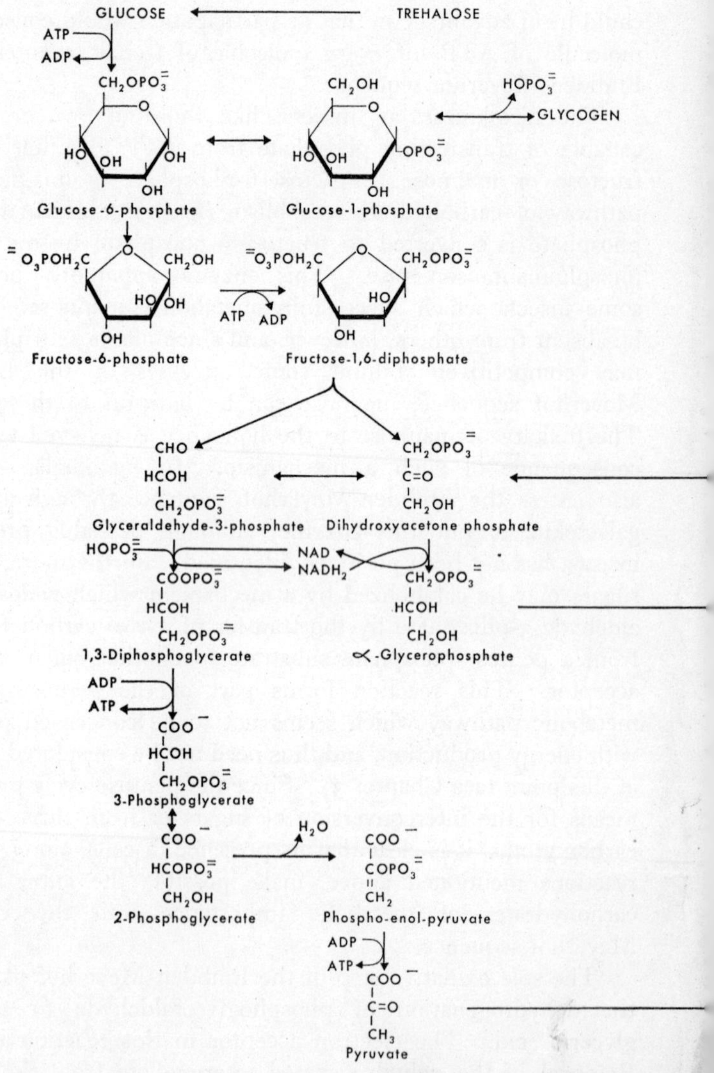

FIG. 1.   Energy production fro

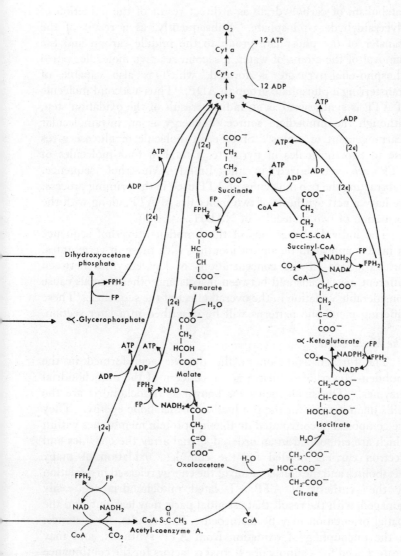

...rbohydrate in flight muscle.

ATP. Thus the first molecule of ATP is synthesized in the catabolism of carbohydrate as a direct result of the oxidation of glyceraldehyde-3-phosphate. Subsequently, as a result of the transfer of the phosphate group to the middle carbon and the removal of the atoms of water, a second reactive molecule, called phospho-enol-pyruvate is formed, which is also capable of transferring a phosphate group to ADP. Thus a second molecule of ATP is synthesized as an indirect result of the oxidation step, although the immediate source of energy is an intramolecular rearrangement of atoms. Since each molecule of glucose gives rise to two molecules of pyruvate, a total of four molecules of ATP are synthesized in the Embden-Meyerhof sequence. Subtracting the two molecules of ATP used in the priming process, we have a nett synthesis of two molecules of ATP, along with the formation of two molecules of $NADH_2$.

The individual reactions of the Embden-Meyerhof sequence in insects appear to be almost identical with those in vertebrates, but variations in the concentrations of key enzymes between different insect cells and between insects and other animals cause considerable variation in the overall effect of the sequence. These differing metabolic patterns will be described in a later section.

The Krebs Cycle

The further oxidation of the pyruvic acid formed in the Embden-Meyerhof sequence is the concern of the mitochondrial enzymes. The small inclusions known as mitochondria are the cell's main centres for the production of metabolic energy. They are composed of convoluted double lipoprotein membranes within which are embedded in an ordered spatial array the enzymes and electron carriers needed for the complete oxidation of many metabolites and the conservation of the energy released in oxidation by the synthesis of ATP. Isolated mitochondria are easily damaged, with the result that essential parts may leak out, and the spatial orientation may be disturbed. This results, for instance, in the uncoupling of oxidation from ATP synthesis, and may create a need for a supply of external cofactors for the continuance of some reactions. On the other hand, disruption allows some of the individual reactions to be studied in isolation. With increasing knowledge of the factors responsible for mitochondrial integrity, more and more insight has been gained into the way in which individual reactions are linked together into a metabolic unit, which permits the uninterrupted flow of electrons from substrate to oxygen and conserves energy by the esterification of phosphate. There are, however, still many important gaps in our knowledge of how the mitochondrion works.

Of recent years, important contributions to knowledge of oxidative mechanisms have stemmed from studies on the isolated mitochondria of insects, in particular the giant mitochondria, or sarcosomes, of 'fibrillar' flight muscle, which will be described more fully in later sections. Since the flight muscles of insects consume energy at an extraordinarily high rate during flight, it is understandable that the mitochondria of these tissues should prove attractive subjects for the study of oxidative mechanisms. For some years the great fragility of the flight muscle sarcosomes hampered research. More recently, however, information has accumulated which has been of considerable significance for the understanding of both insect metabolism and of oxidative mechanisms in general. Many of the results of this work will be considered both in this section and in the treatment of terminal oxidation.

Many individual reactions participate in the complete oxidation of pyruvic acid to carbon dioxide and water. These are linked with one another in a true metabolic cycle called the Krebs citric acid cycle or the tricarboxylic acid cycle (T.C.A. cycle) which is illustrated in figure 1. This cycle, besides effecting the oxidation of pyruvate, provides a mechanism for the interconversion of many organic acids of biological importance. It thus plays a very important rôle in intermediate metabolism in general as well as in catabolism. Several of the reactions of the Krebs cycle involve the combination of the substrate with a coenzyme not previously mentioned in this chapter, and one of immense significance in both catabolic and biosynthetic mechanisms. This is coenzyme A (CoA), a molecule which includes in its structure the vitamin pantothenic acid, the phosphate derivative of which is attached in pyrophosphate linkage to an adenine nucleotide carrying an additional phosphate group on the third carbon atom of its ribose portion. Both CoA and NAD play a part in the first step of pyruvate oxidation catalysed by the enzyme pyruvic dehydrogenase, the end products of which are acetyl coenzyme A (acetyl-S-CoA), $NADH_2$ and CO_2. The pyrophosphate ester of the vitamin thiamin is a coenzyme in this reaction. Three vitamins, pantothenic acid, thiamin and nicotinamide, thus play a part in this key reaction of carbohydrate catabolism. Insects, like other animals must obtain these compounds preformed in the diet, although some species draw their supplies from micro-organisms which they harbour in their alimentary canals, or even within their own cells.

Acetyl-S-CoA, the substrate for the Krebs cycle, is also the main end product of the oxidation of long-chain fatty acids, so that at this point the pathways for the oxidation of carbohydrate and fat converge. Moreover, the carbon skeletons of a number of amino acids are either intermediates of the Krebs cycle, or may readily be converted to them. The cycle thus acts as a common pathway for the catabolism of the three main divisions of food-stuffs, and as well makes possible the conversion of carbohydrate to fat or protein. Acetyl-S-CoA may also be formed directly from acetic acid in a reaction which involves the splitting of ATP to AMP and pyrophosphate:

$$\text{acetic acid} + \text{CoA} + \text{ATP} \longrightarrow \text{acetyl-}S\text{-CoA} + \text{AMP} + \text{PP}.$$

In the first reaction of the Krebs cycle acetyl-S-CoA condenses with oxaloacetate to form the tricarboxylic acid citrate. Citrate is subjected to a number of dehydrogenations and decarboxylations in a series of enzymic reactions which proceed until oxaloacetate is regenerated, and the cycle returns to its starting point. In the first of these dehydrogenations, catalysed by iso-citric dehydrogenase, NADP is the electron acceptor; in the second, catalysed by α-ketoglutaric dehydrogenase, NAD is the electron acceptor. Coenzyme A re-enters the cycle in this reaction, which, like the dehydrogenation of pyruvate, also involves a decarboxylation. The energy released in the cleavage of the thio-ester linkage of the succinyl-CoA formed from α-ketoglutarate can be conserved by the binding of inorganic phosphate in ester linkage. Another nucleotide, guanosine diphosphate (GDP), rather than ADP, is the phosphate acceptor in this reaction, but the GTP so formed can transfer phosphate to ADP as the result of the activity of a transphosphorylase widely distributed in living cells.

In the third dehydrogenation of the Krebs cycle, catalysed by succinic dehydrogenase, the electron acceptor is a flavoprotein. The flavoproteins are another important class of oxidation-reduction enzymes, in which the prosthetic group, or coenzyme, is a derivative of the vitamin riboflavin. There are two such coenzymes, flavin mononucleotide (riboflavin phosphate) and flavin-adenine dinucleotide, which, like the other dinucleotide coenzymes, is a double nucleotide held together by a pyrophosphate linkage. In the presence of the appropriate enzymes these coenzymes accept two atoms of hydrogen from the substrate and transfer two electrons to the cytochrome system.

In the final dehydrogenation of the Krebs cycle, catalysed by malic dehydrogenase, NAD is the electron acceptor. Thus the processing of acetyl-S-CoA through one revolution of the cycle results in the synthesis of one molecule of ATP, the evolution of two molecules of CO_2, and the transfer of four pairs of electrons to the nicotinamide or flavin coenzymes.

Krebs cycle reactions are prominent in insect flight muscle,[58, 24] and it is clear that the pathway plays just as important a part in oxidative energy production in this tissue as it does in the flight muscle of birds, where most of the reactions were originally studied. Some attempts to demonstrate the Krebs cycle in larval tissues, or in adult fat body, have not been successful. Such negative findings may well be due in part to unexpected technical difficulties, but the possibility still remains that the lower energy demands of such tissues may be satisfied by alternative mechanisms.

Before considering the passage of the electrons removed from the substrate in the Embden-Meyerhof sequence and the Krebs cycle to their eventual union with oxygen, it is appropriate that at this stage we study the steps in the oxidation of fat, the second major source of energy for insect activity. Fat is catabolized by a pathway which merges in its final stages with the pathway for the catabolism of carbohydrate.

Oxidation of Fat

Although it is obvious that fat is an important source of energy in insects, our knowledge of the mechanisms by which it is oxidized is far from complete. It is known that the flight muscles of insects which burn fat in flight contain the enzyme lipase, which hydrolyses the triglyceride fats into their component fatty acids and the alcohol glycerol. It will be seen that glycerol, once phosphorylated, can be oxidized rapidly in flight muscle. However, only some of the enzymatic steps by which fatty acids are degraded have been studied in insects, and the existence of others must be inferred from work with other animals. For several years, investigators were unable to demonstrate any appreciable *in vitro* oxidation of fatty acids by flight muscle mitochondria. The difficulties associated with this work have since been overcome, and it is now known that the mitochondria of locust flight muscle, in particular, are capable of the rapid oxidation of fatty acids. Some of the difficulty in demonstrating fatty acid oxidation by mitochondria may have been due in part to a failure of the free fatty acids to bind to the sites of oxidation within the mitochondria. Recent work with vertebrate mitochondria has demonstrated that fatty acids conjugated with the nitrogenous base carnitine are oxidized much more rapidly than when they are in the free state. This points to a rôle for carnitine, an essential metabolite first recognized as a vitamin for certain insects, in fatty acid metabolism. Carnitine had been known for many years as a component of animal tissues, but it was not until it was identified as an essential nutrient for beetles of the genus *Tenebrio* that it was realized that it played a vital rôle in animal metabolism, Just what that rôle is has been the subject of much fruitless study, but now it seems that carnitine might provide a key to the understanding of the catabolism of fats, a very important facet of insect metabolism about which all too little is known. Another factor which has hindered the study of fatty acid oxidation in insects is the harmful effect exerted by free fatty acids on the structural integrity of mitochondria. Fatty acids released during the grinding of the tissue were found to be responsible for much of the malfunctioning of the mitochondria in early preparations, and it was not until serum albumen, which combined with the fatty acids, was used in the isolating medium that intact mitochondria were obtained. This fragility affects all mitochondria, but those of insects seem to be more sensitive than most.

The sequence of events in the oxidation of fatty acids as it is known in animal and plant tissues, called the β-oxidation pathway, is illustrated in figure 2. The first step is combination with coenzyme A, after which the acyl-CoA derivative undergoes two dehydrogenations to form a compound with a keto group in the β position. Another molecule of CoA then participates in a so-called 'thiolytic' cleavage at this position, resulting in the

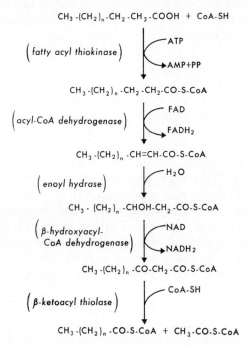

FIG. 2.   Pathway of oxidation of fatty acids.

formation of acetyl-CoA and the CoA derivative of the fatty acid chain, now reduced by two carbon units. The last two enzymes in this sequence have been identified in locust flight muscle mitochondria.[23] In *Locusta migratoria* these two enzymes increase in activity during the development of the wing muscles more than any other mitochondrial enzymes and thus assume an importance to be expected in insects which consume large quantities of fat in migratory flights.

When the fatty acid to be oxidized contains an even number

of carbon atoms it can be split completely into acetyl-S-CoA units, but when there is an odd number of carbon atoms one of the end products is a three-carbon unit, propionyl-S-CoA. Propionyl-S-CoA is metabolized in mammals by the addition of carbon dioxide, and eventual conversion to succinyl-S-CoA, but its fate in insect tissues has not been studied. Acetyl-S-CoA and succinyl-S-CoA can be oxidized completely by entering the Krebs cycle, in which the pathways for the catabolism of carbohydrate, fat and amino acids converge.

Oxidation of Amino Acids

The discovery that the amino acids in the blood may constitute an energy reserve in some insects is so recent[9] that little information is available on the catabolic pathways involved. Proline disappears from the blood of the tsetse fly during flight, and is quantitatively replaced by alanine. This conversion is accompanied by a small rise in the concentration of α-ketoglutarate in the blood. Since there is no accumulation of nitrogenous excretory products, it seems probable that proline loses its amino group by transamination, and that only its carbon skeleton is catabolized. An oxidative conversion of proline to glutamic acid, which is known to occur in other animals, may be the first step in the pathway. Transamination from glutamate to pyruvate, a reaction

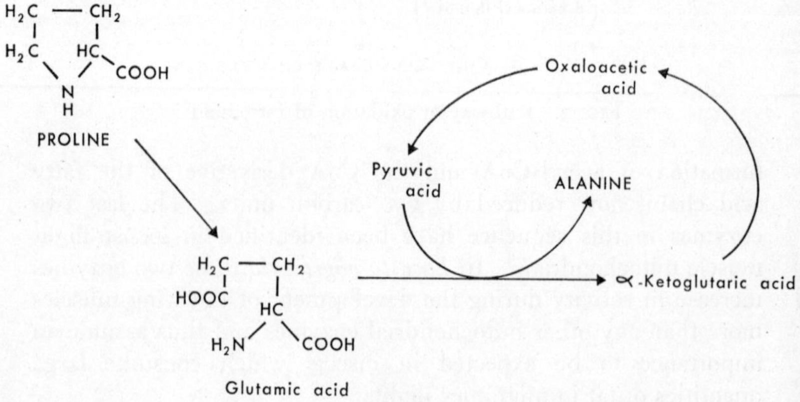

FIG. 3. Proposed energy-production cycle of adult tsetse fly.

readily performed by insects, would lead to the production of alanine and α-ketoglutarate, of which the latter would be oxidized through the Krebs cycle. This suggested pathway is illustrated in figure 3. It emphasizes, once again, the importance of the Krebs cycle in the interconversion of the major cell metabolites and its involvement as the ultimate mechanism of aerobic energy production.

A rôle for proline as energy reserve may be of quite general occurrence in insects, since it is known that one of the effects of DDT poisoning in several species is a decrease in the concentration of proline in the blood and an increase in alanine. Since DDT produces hyperactivity, it is possible that the decrease in proline indicates an exhaustion of energy reserves by the insects' overactive muscles.

Terminal Oxidation

Components of the electron transport chain

The mitochondria, which contain the enzymes of the Krebs cycle and the fatty acid oxidation pathway, also have built into their structure the complex of proteins and lipids which undertake the transfer of the pairs of electrons removed from the substrate in successive dehydrogenations to their final union with oxygen, simultaneously trapping the energy released in this process by the phosphorylation of ADP. The protein components of this system have been studied for many years, and although technical problems have hampered attempts at isolating and characterizing them, great advances have been made in understanding their functions. The lipid components have only recently become the subject of intense study, and our knowledge of their function is more limited.

The main protein components of the chain in the mitochondria of all animal tissues so far studied are the flavoproteins and the cytochromes. The flavoproteins, as mentioned earlier, have flavin prosthetic groups, while the cytochromes have iron-porphyrin (haem) prosthetic groups. The central iron atom of the porphyrin nucleus of each cytochrome is capable of reversible oxidation-reduction ($Fe^{++} \rightarrow Fe^{+++} + \epsilon$), and since the cytochromes are arranged in a series of ascending oxidation-reduction potential, the reduced form of one cytochrome is able to pass electrons to the oxidized form of the next highest cytochrome in the chain. Thus electrons can flow without interruption along the chain towards eventual union with oxygen, releasing free energy with every rise in the state of oxidation. There are three main groups of cytochromes: cytochromes b, which are capable of accepting electrons from reduced flavoprotein, cytochromes c, which occupy an intermediate position, and cytochromes a, which are capable of transferring electrons to oxygen. Individual variations are found within this grouping, some, as we will see, being characteristic of certain insect tissues, but the same general plan seems to apply to all aerobic cells throughout the animal and plant kingdoms. Since the protein components, and also NAD (which is involved in many of the individual pathways of electron transfer), all show characteristic changes in absorption spectrum in passing from the oxidized to the reduced state, the study of the absorption spectra of either living cells or of suspensions of isolated mitochondria has been one of the most fruitful methods of studying the electron transfer chain.

Coenzyme Q₉

Of the lipid components of the chain, the compounds called ubiquinones have received the most attention. The chemical structure of the ubiquinones is that of a quinone nucleus to which is attached a long hydrocarbon side chain containing between thirty and fifty carbon atoms. The side chain is made up of units, each containing five carbon atoms, known as isoprenes, which, as we will see later, are structural components of a number of hydrocarbons of biological importance, such as terpenes, sterols and carotenoids. Ubiquinones are also known by the general name of coenzyme Q, and are designated Q_6 to Q_{10}, according to the number of isoprene units in the side chain. The ubiquinone of most insects is Q_9, although Q_{10}, the characteristic ubiquinone of mammals, has also been isolated from insects. Insect flight muscle, which is extremely rich in the protein components of the electron transport chain, also has one of the highest concentrations of ubiquinone of any living tissue. It has been established that ubiquinones are components of the electron transport chain, since removal of ubiquinone from the chain can interrupt electron transfer and its subsequent addition can restore it. Moreover, there is evidence that the quinone undergoes oxidation and reduction during the flow of electrons through the chain. There is still no certainty, however, about the precise function of the lipid coenzymes. It has been suggested that both the ubiquinones, and derivatives of vitamin K (which also have a quinone structure and have been proposed as members of the electron transport chain) may have a function in the coupling of oxidation with the phosphorylation of ADP, but convincing evidence in support of this proposal has not been found.

Mitochondria contain a number of other lipids, which are believed to provide the proper hydrophobic environment within which directed electron flow can occur. Particularly important from this point of view in mammalian mitochondria are the phospholipids, but preliminary studies of the lipids of some insect flight muscle mitochondria have shown that phospholipids are virtually absent. Much more knowledge of the chemistry and function of mitochondrial lipids will be needed before such differences can be related to the varying behaviour of mitochondria from different sources.

From the very beginning of research into the function of the haem pigments insects have figured prominently as study material. It was soon recognized that perhaps the heaviest concentration of these pigments in any tissue is to be found in the thoracic muscles of flying insects, and, moreover, occurs there in an environment uncontaminated by the blood pigment haemoglobin. So KEILIN,[39] for example, was able to see the absorption bands of the cytochromes in living muscle by removing the scales from the thorax of the wax moth, *Galleria*, and observing the muscles through the transparent cuticle. Thus the accumulation of knowledge of the cytochromes of insect cells has kept pace with, and sometimes outstripped, that of mammalian cytochromes.

The protein components of the electron transport chain, and the direction of electron flow in the mitochondria of insect muscles[60, 24] are shown in figure 4. Three enzymes with typical flavoprotein absorption spectra transfer electrons to cytochrome b. The first of these accepts hydrogen from the $NADH_2$ formed by the several NAD-linked dehydrogenases of the mitochondrion; the second accepts hydrogen from α-glycerophosphate, which is thereby oxidized to dihydroxyacetone phosphate; the third accepts hydrogen from succinate, oxidizing it to fumarate. Cytochromes b, c and a of insect mitochondria appear to be identical in function and in absorption spectrum with the corresponding mammalian cytochromes. Only cytochrome c is easily isolated and purified in solution, and it seems certain that the prosthetic group of this cytochrome, at least, is exactly the same as its mammalian counterpart. In fact, it has been shown that the amino acid sequence of the part of the protein in close

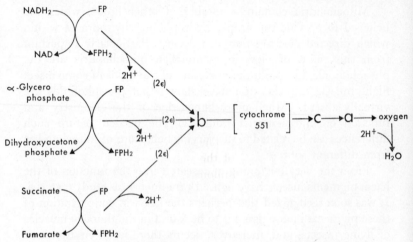

FIG. 4.   Electron transport chain of insect mitochondria.

association with the iron porphyrin is very nearly the same, though not quite identical, with that of beef heart cytochrome c.

Some doubt exists as to whether one or two cytochromes are engaged in electron transport at the oxidation-reduction potential of cytochrome a. For several years it has been believed that cytochrome a itself transfers electrons to another haem protein, which effects the final union with oxygen. The evidence for this duality was the fact that combination of the terminal cytochrome with carbon monoxide (which inhibits tissue respiration at this point) changed only one of the two absorption band ascribed to the a complex. The cytochrome which combined with carbon monoxide was called cytochrome a_3, or cytochrome oxidase, and was thus equated with the *Atmungsferment* of WARBURG, who had pioneered the important work on the effect of carbon monoxide on the terminal oxidase of tissues, and the reversal of these effects by light. But attempts to isolate two haem pigments at the oxidation-reduction potential of cytochrome a have not been successful, and it is now suspected that the spectroscopic changes observed may emanate from a single cytochrome.

The existence of a second cytochrome in the c region, although also inferred from spectroscopic evidence, is more firmly established. The absorption maxima of cytochrome c and its companion, which is called cytochrome c_1, become separable only when the tissue extracts are examined at the temperature of liquid nitrogen. At this temperature, the absorption maxima of reduced cytochrome c of mammalian preparations lie at 545 and 548 mμ, while that of cytochrome c_1 is at 554 mμ. The separation of these closely similar spectra in spectroscopic studies is made possible by the sharpening and intensification of the absorption peaks which occur at the low temperature and by the fact that it is possible to wash all the cytochrome c from the mitochondria, thus leaving a preparation which exhibits the spectrum of the remaining cytochromes b, c_1 and a. Cytochrome c in insect preparations is, as stated above, identical with that of vertebrates, and has absorption maxima at 545 and 548 mμ, but no pigment with the same properties of the cytochrome c_1 of mammals has yet been identified. Mitochondria of housefly flight muscle possess a cytochrome with an absorption maximum at 551 mμ when reduced physiologically by the substrate, and the same preparation exhibits a peak at 555 mμ when reduced chemically by dithionate. The latter spectrum has also been recorded in mitochondria from the muscles of the cecropia moth, *Hyalophora cecropia*. What relationship the pigment or pigments with these absorption spectra have with the cytochrome c_1 of mammals remains to be determined.

The passage of electrons through the electron transport chain is accompanied by the phosphorylation of ADP. One molecule of ATP is formed during the transfer of a pair of electrons from $NADH_2$ through flavoprotein to cytochrome b, and a further two molecules are synthesized with the passage of a pair of electrons from cytochrome b through cytochromes c_1, c and a to oxygen. When electrons move from either succinate or α-glycerophosphate

M.I.—C

directly to cytochrome b, no ATP is synthesized, so the complete passage of a pair of electrons from either of these substrates to oxygen results in the formation of only two molecules of ATP. In carefully prepared mitochondria this coupling of electron transport with ATP synthesis is very tight, and such mitochondria consume very little oxygen even in the presence of oxidizable substrates unless ADP is added as a phosphate acceptor. Conversely, the addition of ATP may drive the electron flow in such preparations in the reverse direction in parts of the chain, so that reductions, rather than oxidations, are performed. Although a great deal is known about the extent of ATP synthesis during terminal oxidation, and the effect of varying conditions on it, the molecular mechanism of this process of energy conservation is obscure.

Respiratory mechanisms of insect muscle

The flight muscles of insects are extraordinarily well adapted for aerobic respiration. They have an abundant supply of well ventilated tracheae which penetrate the muscle cells and come into close contact with the mitochondria, thus carrying oxygen in gaseous form almost right up to the point at which it is used. The muscle cells contain numerous mitochondria, which are packed with enzymes capable of carrying out the complete oxidation of many substrates. In some of the higher insect orders, particularly those in which high wing-beat frequencies (100 to 1000 strokes per second) are encountered, the flight muscles are of a special histological type, known as fibrillar muscle. In these muscles the myofibrils are of large diameter and are arranged in parallel groups separated by columns of tightly packed mitochondria of unusually large size (5 micra or more in diameter). These mitochondria oxidize substrates and supply ATP to the fibrils, against which they are tightly pressed, at the high rate needed to maintain the immense energy output of sustained flight.

The effectiveness of this aerobic respiration is nowhere seen to better advantage than in the flight muscles of those flies, such as the housefly and some blowflies, which burn carbohydrate exclusively in flight. The rate of oxygen consumption of these insects may rise by one hundred or more times during flight, yet at the end of a period of flight the respiratory rate drops almost immediately to its resting value. This is in marked contrast to the situation in mammals, in which a heightened respiratory rate persists for some time after a period of exercise. The main reason for this difference is undoubtedly the great concentration of oxidative enzymes in the insect tissue, and the effective transport of oxygen to the sites of oxidation, so that the anaerobic phase of glucose catabolism, the Embden-Meyerhof sequence, never outstrips the aerobic processes, but the adaptation of insect flight muscle to this intensely aerobic respiration has resulted in some unique features in its respiratory mechanisms which will be examined in the following pages.

Early work on the respiration of the large mitochondria, or sarcosomes, of fibrillar muscle established one outstanding characteristic—they oxidized α-glycerophosphate much more rapidly than any other substrate.[61] Rates of oxidation of pyruvate, succinate, or other Krebs cycle intermediates, which are preferred substrates for most mammalian mitochondria, were relatively low, so low, in fact, that for some time the absorption spectrum of $NADH_2$, which would have been expected to show up in the presence of Krebs cycle substrates, could not be detected. Subsequent studies have shown that the differences between insect and mammalian mitochondria are not as great as at first thought. It is now known that flight muscle mitochondria can oxidize Krebs cycle intermediates at a fast rate; some of the early difficulties seem to have been due to the failure of substrates to penetrate the mitochondria. Moreover, re-examination of the mitochondria of mammalian muscle has shown that the α-glycerophosphate pathway is not without significance in these preparations also, but nevertheless, the extraordinary rapidity of α-glycerophosphate oxidation remains the outstanding feature of the flight muscle mitochondria.

The enzyme responsible for this oxidation is the cytochrome-linked flavoprotein α-glycerophosphate dehydrogenase. But flight muscle contains another α-glycerophosphate dehydrogenase, situated in the sarcoplasm. This soluble enzyme performs the reversible oxidation of α-glycerophosphate to dihydroxyacetone phosphate by transferring electrons to and from NAD. The presence of two enzymes apparently performing the same function in two different compartments of the cell provided the clue to the significance of the α-glycerophosphate pathway in flight muscle.

It had been known for some time that mitochondria were unable to oxidize $NADH_2$ added externally in solution—apparently $NADH_2$ could not penetrate the mitochondrion to the sites of oxidation. But for every molecule of glucose consumed in the cell, one molecule of $NADH_2$ is formed in the cytoplasm by the action of the enzyme glyceraldehyde-3-phosphate dehydrogenase (fig. 1), and unless this coenzyme is immediately reoxidized by the transfer of electrons to another acceptor, energy production must cease. In mammalian muscle, and, as we shall see, in some insect muscle, pyruvate acts as the electron acceptor, being reduced to lactate by the action of the enzyme lactic dehydrogenase. In insect flight muscle, however, lactic dehydrogenase has a very low activity, and its function is taken over by the soluble α-glycerophosphate dehydrogenase. Thus dihydroxyacetone phosphate accepts electrons from $NADH_2$ and is reduced to α-glycerophosphate, while NAD is restored for participation in the main Embden-Meyerhof pathway. The α-glycerophosphate so formed diffuses readily into the mitochondria, where it is reoxidized by the powerful α-glycerophosphate dehydrogenase present there, transferring electrons through the cytochromes to oxygen. The dihydroxyacetone formed in this reaction diffuses out of the mitochondria to complete the cycle, and is then ready to accept electrons once more. Thus the two α-glycerophosphate dehydrogenases and their substrates act as a powerful catalytic cycle whereby reducing equivalents (electrons) derived initially from glyceraldehyde-3-phosphate are fed into the mitochondrial electron transport system, thus making possible the rapid and complete oxidation of glucose to carbon dioxide and water within the muscle cell. This operation of the α-glycerophosphate cycle between the cytoplasmic and mitochondrial compartments of the cell is illustrated in figure 1.

Duplication of another enzyme system also occurs in flight muscle. Malic dehydrogenase, which oxidizes malate to oxaloacetate, is present as an NAD-linked enzyme in the cytoplasm, and is also found linked to the cytochromes in the mitochondria. The two malic dehydrogenases and their substrates could thus set up a catalytic cycle similar to the α-glycerophosphate cycle, and it is possible that such a system is important in some tissues, but present evidence suggests that the malate system is of only minor importance in the oxidation of extramitochondrial $NADH_2$ in flight muscle, because of the overwhelming activity of the α-glycerophosphate cycle.

Now we can see why flies do not need a heightened respiration of recovery after a period of flight. All of the many individual steps in the catabolism of glucose are integrated with the shuttling of reducing equivalents through the cytochromes to oxygen. This complete interlocking of the whole catabolic process in the presence of a plentiful supply of oxygen means that only the supply of the carbohydrate substrate limits the energy output of the muscle, and, in fact, it has been shown that in the blowfly *Phormia* the wing beat frequency and hence the power output varies directly with the concentration of trehalose in the blood. The only end products are carbon dioxide and water, and nothing remains to be dealt with when exercise stops. In mammals, by contrast, the blood is unable to transport oxygen to the muscles at a rate fast enough to satisfy energy demands during exercise. Here the α-glycerophosphate pathway is less important, and lactic dehydrogenase assumes the function of reoxidizing the $NADH_2$ formed in the oxidation of glyceraldehyde-3-phosphate. Thereby, pyruvate is reduced to lactate, the reactions of the Embden-Meyerhof sequence are effectively uncoupled from mitochondrial oxidation, and the muscle is said to go into oxygen debt. The lactic acid formed in the muscle is transported to the liver, where it is partly burned and partly resynthesized to glycogen. This process goes on long after exercise has ceased and accounts for the extra respiration of recovery, as the animal ' pays off ' its oxygen debt.

By no means all insect muscles share the ability to stay out of debt for oxygen shown by the flight muscles of some flies. Butterflies and moths, which seem to have an obligatory requirement for fat as the fuel for flight,[50] exhibit a heightened recovery respiration which may persist for more than an hour after a flight of only ten minutes. The desert locust, which burns both carbohydrate and fat during flight, incurs a similar, though perhaps somewhat smaller, oxygen debt. Since the metabolic pathways for the oxidation of fat have not been studied in detail in these insects, it is not possible to relate their respiratory exchange either during flight or in the recovery process to metabolic events within the muscle. It is possible, however, that the extra respiration of recovery is concerned with the removal of ketone bodies (aceto-acetate, β-hydroxybutyrate, acetone), which are known to accumulate in other animals as a result of the incomplete oxidation of fatty acids. Accumulation of such metabolites would suggest an imbalance in the rates of the reactions leading to the production of acetyl-S-CoA and those concerned with the oxidation of acetyl-S-CoA through the Krebs cycle.

Two contrasting muscle types occur in locusts, and have been studied particularly in *Locusta migratoria*.[78] In this species, the flight muscles, though not of the fibrillar type, have plentiful large mitochondria and an extensive supply of tracheae which penetrate the muscle cells. The jumping muscle of the hind femora have smaller, less numerous mitochondria, and a reduced tracheal supply ending on the exterior of the muscle cells. The activity of the cytoplasmic α-glycerophosphate dehydrogenase of the flight muscle is one hundred times greater than that of the lactic dehydrogenase, and it is clear that these muscles, like the flight muscles of the housefly, are geared for the oxidation of extramitochondrial $NADH_2$, and the complete oxidative cata-bolism of carbohydrate substrates. In the jumping muscle, on the other hand, the relative activities of the two dehydrogenases are reversed, and here the metabolic changes accompanying activity are very much the same as in mammalian skeletal muscle, practically all of the glycogen used being accounted for by the accumulation of lactic acid, with only a very minor increase in α-glycerophosphate. These metabolic differences are obviously related to the differing functions of the two muscles—sustained energy output at a high rate in the case of the flight muscle, and occasional powerful twitches with ample time for recovery in the case of the femoral muscle. Since the α-glycerophosphate pathway is so well developed in the flight muscles of the migratory locust, it seems likely that the coupling of the Embden-Meyerhof pathway with mitochondrial oxidation would be as effective in this muscle as it is in the flight muscle of the housefly. This suggests that any repayment of the oxygen debt after flight in this insect, or in the related desert locust, *Schistocerca gregaria*, is not likely to be connected with carbohydrate metabolism, but rather, as suggested above, with the removal of metabolites accumulated during the oxidation of fat.

Another puzzling feature of insect flight muscle mitochondria which impressed earlier workers in this field was their failure to exhibit ' respiratory control ' by ADP. Mitochondria from other muscles which have been isolated with care, and in which electron transport is tightly coupled with phosphorylation, oxidize substrates at only a very low rate unless ADP is supplied to act as an acceptor of phosphate esterified in the electron transport chain. During muscle contraction ATP is dephosphorylated to ADP, which diffuses into the mitochondria and stimulates oxidation. The concentration of ADP is thus seen as the primary factor controlling the rate of respiration, and the degree to which added ADP increases the oxygen uptake of isolated mitochondria is a measure of their respiratory control. The difference between resting and active respiratory rates is so great in flight muscle that it is clear that an effective mechanism for controlling electron flow through the mitochondria must exist. It appears that the early failure to demonstrate respiratory control in flight muscle mitochondria was due, in part, to damage to the structure during isolation, and in the latest report control factors for ADP as high as 25 have been recorded, with pyruvate as the substrate for oxidation. This figure is within the range needed to account for the difference between resting and active respiratory rates, but flight muscle, in fact, possesses an additional control mechanism. It has been shown that the rate of oxidation of α-glycerophosphate by the mitochondria is strongly inhibited by the accumulation of the oxidation product, dihydroxyacetone phosphate, and only becomes appreciable when the ratio of the concentration of substrate to that of product is more than 3·0. Thus the complete control system and its operation during the change from rest to activity are thought to be as follows: with the onset of activity, ADP diffuses into the mitochondria and stimulates oxidation of pyruvate; decrease in pyruvate concentration activates the enzymes of the Embden-Meyerhof sequence, which in turn, because of the coupling of the glyceraldehyde phosphate dehydrogenase with the cytoplasmic α-glycerophosphate dehydrogenase, leads to a rise in α-glycerophosphate concentration. The consequent alteration in the α-glycerophosphate/dihydroxyacetone phosphate ratio stimulates the mitochondrial α-glycerophosphate oxidase, further increasing mitochondrial respiration as electrons derived from phosphoglyceraldehyde are passed to oxygen. When muscular contraction ceases, ATP concentration rises and stops pyruvate oxidation. The accumulation of pyruvate stops the Embden-Meyerhof sequence and the build up of dihydroxy-acetone phosphate shuts off the a-glycerophosphate oxidase.

Anaerobic Energy Metabolism

Although most insects are extremely well adapted to aerobic life, they are also capable of surviving for quite long periods of time in the absence of oxygen. A few insects pursue an active life under anaerobic conditions, but aerobic forms are rapidly rendered immobile by oxygen lack, and in this state may survive for several hours in a situation which is fatal to most mammals in a few minutes. Presumably one reason for this resistance may be a relatively low sensitivity of the insect's nervous system to the harmful effects of the accumulating metabolites of anaerobic energy production, or to the breakdown of cytochrome-linked mechanisms in their membranes. There is, however, some evidence to suggest that insects may derive their energy anaerobic-ally by mechanisms unknown in mammals. Nevertheless, the dismutation of glucose to pyruvate by the Embden-Meyerhof pathway, which is a major mechanism of anaerobic energy production in organisms of all classes, does play an important part in insects. However, since the means of reoxidation of the $NADH_2$ formed in the Embden-Meyerhof sequence is different in many insect tissues from that encountered in other animals, the end products of the anaerobic operation of this pathway in insects are unusual.

In flight muscle, as we have seen, it is a-glycerophosphate dehydrogenase, rather than lactic dehydrogenase which is linked with glyceraldehyde-3-phosphate dehydrogenase through NAD. Thus for every molecule of phosphoglyceric acid formed in the oxidative step of the Embden-Meyerhof sequence a molecule of dihydroxyacetone phosphate is reduced to a-glycerophosphate (fig. 5), and the end products of anaerobic glucose catabolism are equimolar amounts of pyruvate and a-glycerophosphate. It is clear, however, that an enzyme pattern such as this produces only half the energy generated by the more usual sequence leading to lactic acid, since half the triose resulting from the splitting of fructose diphosphate is used in reoxidizing the reduced co-enzyme. In fact, in the cycle as shown in figure 5 there is no overall gain in ATP, since two molecules are used in the formation of fructose diphosphate and two are formed in the reactions leading from diphosphoglycerate to pyruvate. Only when glycogen is the substrate is there any nett gain in energy. Thus anaerobic

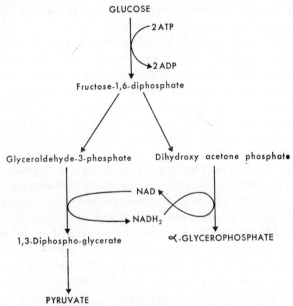

FIG. 5. Anaerobic metabolism of flight muscle.

glycolysis in insects is much less efficient than in vertebrates, a disadvantage which, for insects, is obviously outweighed by the advantage inherent in a system which effectively couples the cytoplasmic and mitochondrial phases of carbohydrate catabolism during aerobic energy production.

Some insect tissues, such as the midgut, and the femoral muscles of locusts, mentioned earlier, contain active lactic dehydrogenases, and here the conventional pathway of anaerobic glycolysis is active, with two molecules of lactic acid formed for every molecule of glucose used. Analysis of whole insects after periods of anoxia have confirmed that all three of the end products mentioned, α-glycerophosphate, pyruvate and lactate, accumulate as glycogen or sugars disappear. It seems clear from this that the relative amounts of the end products appearing in any one tissue are controlled by the relative activities of the α-glycerophosphate and lactic dehydrogenases. In very few instances, however, have the total amounts of the three end products accounted for all the glycogen disappearing during anaerobiosis. It is probable that other pathways, in addition to those already mentioned, play a part in anaerobic energy production.

Of course, in the complete absence of oxygen it is inevitable that all the electron carriers and coenzymes of electron transfer will become fully reduced. Under these circumstances a number of reductions may occur which are not normally part of the energy-providing reactions. Any metabolite or enzyme system which can act as an alternate electron acceptor in the absence of oxygen may have some value in permitting the continued turnover of nucleotide coenzymes. Some mechanisms of this kind will be considered in the next section, on respiration in diapause.

A recent attempt to determine products of anaerobic metabolism in insects has shown that pyruvate accumulates rapidly during the early part of anaerobiosis, but that later its concentration falls.[56] One metabolite which increases in concentration as pyruvate disappears is alanine. It is suggested that a mechanism may exist for the reoxidation of $NADH_2$ by the conversion of pyruvate to alanine by the action of the two enzymes transaminase and glutamic dehydrogenase, as follows:

$$\text{pyruvate} + \text{glutamate} \longrightarrow \text{alanine} + \alpha\text{-ketoglutarate}$$
$$\alpha\text{-ketoglutarate} + NADH_2 + NH_3 \longrightarrow \text{glutamate} + NAD$$

$$\text{sum: pyruvate} + NADH_2 + NH_3 \longrightarrow \text{alanine} + NAD$$

However, it seems that not all the alanine formed during this period is derived from pyruvate, and other reactions must also be taking place.

A number of anaerobic bacteria are capable of using amino acids as both electron donors and electron acceptors, and at least one such reaction, the reductive deamination of glycine by $NADH_2$ to yield acetate and ammonia, is known to conserve

energy by the formation of ATP.   Since free amino acids are
present in extraordinarily high concentration in insect blood, it is
clear that the substrates for such anaerobic mechanisms would be
readily available, and the pryuvate formed in the Embden-
Meyerhof sequence might be seen as a convenient acceptor of the
ammonia produced.   None of these reactions is known to occur in
insects, however, and our ideas on anaerobic mechanisms apart
from those associated with the linking of the Embden-Meyerhof
sequence with either lactic or α-glycerophosphate dehydrogenases
are almost completely speculative.

Other possible anaerobic pathways are suggested by studies on
parasitic worms, which live in an environment almost completely
lacking in oxygen.   A number of mechanisms for the further
metabolism of pyruvate formed in the Embden-Meyerhof sequence
have been developed in these animals.   They involve decarboxylation to acetate and condensation with propionate to yield higher
fatty acids, which are excreted.   Another mechanism of considerable importance involves the reoxidation of $NADH_2$ by the
simultaneous reduction of fumarate to succinate.   It will be
recalled that in insect mitochondria the pathways for the transfer
of electrons from $NADH_2$ and succinate converge at the level of
cytochrome b (fig. 4), and that the passage of electrons from
$NADH_2$ to cytochrome b is linked with the phosphorylation of
ADP.   It has been shown that in insect, as in mammalian and plant
mitochondria, it is possible to force the transfer of electrons from
succinate through cytochrome b to NAD by supplying ATP for
the phosphate-linked part of the pathway.   This is the so-called
reversal of oxidative phosphorylation.   If the electron flow is in the
opposite direction, that is, from $NADH_2$ through cytochrome b to
fumarate, then energy will be conserved by the synthesis of ATP.
Electron transport particles isolated from the roundworm,
Ascaris, catalyse an electron flow of this type, although it is not
known whether a cytochrome of the b type is involved.   The
succinate formed as an end product is excreted by the worm.   It
seems quite likely that a similar process could occur in insect
mitochondria.   The initial reaction could be achieved by the
action of the malic enzyme, which is present in insect tissues, and
which catalyses the fixation of carbon dioxide to pyruvate in the
presence of $NADPH_2$, to form malate.   The conversion of malate

to fumarate, and the reduction of fumarate to succinate could then proceed as in figure 6. It may be significant that malate, fumarate and especially succinate, are present in unusually high concentration in the blood of the larva of the botfly, which leads an anaerobic existence in the gut of the horse during part of its life cycle.

There is one serious objection to both the pathway leading from pyruvate to succinate and that mentioned earlier leading from pyruvate to alanine as mechanisms for the reoxidation of the $NADH_2$ formed in the Embden-Meyerhof sequence. That is, that the enzymes involved in both these pathways are located within

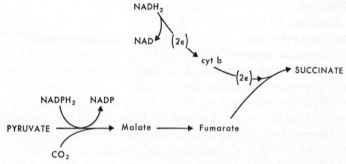

FIG. 6. Suggested pathway of anaerobic energy production.

the mitochondria, whereas the $NADH_2$ is formed in the cytoplasm, and we have already seen that insect mitochondria cannot oxidize external $NADH_2$ directly. The electron transport particles of *Ascaris* are probably not organized into mitochondria, which are normally found only in aerobic organisms, and in the parasitic worms the reoxidation of cytoplasmic $NADH_2$ may present no problem. Perhaps a trace of such mechanisms exists in insects, thus enabling them to survive for a long time in the absence of oxygen. It seems almost certain that in those species with a pronounced ability to withstand anoxia, such as the parasitic botflies and the chironomid larvae, which live in the mud at the bottom of lakes, there must be well developed pathways of anaerobic energy production in addition to those of the Embden-Meyerhof sequence. More work is needed to find out what they are.

Respiration in Diapause

The temporary arrest of development known as diapause plays an important part in the biology of insects. Diapause occurs most frequently in the egg or pupal stages and usually coincides with a period of harsh environmental conditions, such as winter cold. It is marked by a complete cessation of all anabolic processes and a consequent sharp drop in the energy demands of the tissues.[32] The mechanisms by which this metabolic control may be exercised will be discussed in the last chapter of this book. As might be expected, the reduction of energy demands during diapause is marked by a steep fall in the rate of respiration. Less to be expected was the discovery, made many years ago, that the respiration of insects during diapause was unusually insensitive to the action of hydrogen cyanide and carbon monoxide, two powerful poisons which block respiration by combining with the terminal pigment of the electron transport chain, cytochrome a. This seemed to suggest that the respiration of insects in diapause was qualitatively different from that of normally developing individuals, and it was usually concluded that the cytochrome system was somehow by-passed in these respiratory pathways, perhaps by the transfer of electrons directly from flavoprotein dehydrogenases to oxygen. Studies on pupal diapause in the cecropia moth have suggested, however, that the respiration of diapause, although unusual in many respects, may follow the same pathway as in normally developing insects.

At the onset of diapause in *Hyalophora cecropia*, respiration drops to one-fiftieth of its previous rate, and, as in other diapausing insects, becomes resistant to the effects of cyanide and carbon monoxide. The heart beat of the adult insect, for instance, is stopped by a cyanide concentration of about $10^{-5}M$, whereas the pupal heart under comparable conditions is not inhibited until the concentration reaches $10^{-3}M$. At the same time, cytochromes b, c_1 and c apparently disappear from all tissues except those of the intersegmental muscles, which remain normally active. Of the mitochondrial cytochromes, only cytochrome a is detectable, and that in greatly reduced quantities in comparison with non-diapausing tissues. Along with the faint spectrum of cytochrome a appears that of the extramitochondrial cytochrome b_5, the function of which will be discussed later. The beginning of diapause in the egg of the silkworm, however, is not marked by any qualitative change in the cytochrome spectrum. Pre-diapause eggs of the silkworm have cytochromes b_5 and a, which persist during diapause, although the strength of their spectra gradually diminish,[14] perhaps as a result of normal wear and tear in an organism in which the replacement of 'worn out' proteins can no longer be effected. With the resumption of growth at the end of diapause cytochromes b and c make their appearance, as they do in post-diapause development in the cecropia pupa. From a consideration of the cytochrome spectrum then, one would say that diapause in the silkworm represents an abnormal continuation of an early embryonic phase. The apparent reversion to this early embryonic phase in the cecropia moth is probably not so much the result of the loss of individual cytochromes from cells as the loss of larval cells in the normal process of metamorphosis, and their replacement by tissue derived from nests of embryonic cells which persist throughout larval life. It is to be remembered that the intersegmental muscles, which persist from the larva through pupal diapause, retain their full complement of mitochondrial cytochromes. Perhaps only the pupal cells which are still in an embryonic phase of development are sensitive to the blocking action of the diapause mechanism. The same change in cytochrome spectrum that occurs with the release of diapause is seen during the normal development of the adult wing muscles in the honeybee, a development which takes place during late pupal and early adult life in this insect. At an early phase in development, probably when the proteins of the myofibrils are being manufactured, cytochromes b_5 and a are prominent. Later this cytochrome spectrum is replaced by the typical mitochondrial cytochrome pattern as the sarcosomes of the adult muscle are formed.

Cytochrome b_5 was first detected in the tissues of diapausing insects, and because of its prominence there was considered a likely candidate for the rôle of the cyanide-insensitive terminal oxidase of diapause. In fact, no evidence was found to support this idea, and subsequent work showed that b_5 was a normal constituent of many tissues in both vertebrates and invertebrates. It is located in the cytoplasmic reticulum, the system of lipoprotein membranes which form part of the structure of all cells, and which, on rupture of the cell, breaks up into the small particles called microsomes. Insect and mammalian cells contain a flavo-protein enzyme, $NADH_2$-cytochrome b_5 reductase, which specifically catalyses the transfer of electrons to cytochrome b_5, while the reduced cytochrome is itself capable of transferring electrons to oxygen at a slow rate, although its natural electron acceptor in the cell is probably not oxygen, but some metabolite as yet unknown. Because of its location in the endoplasmic reticulum of many cells, cytochrome b_5 is thought to have a general function not related to the special respiration of diapausing tissues. It may play a part in ion transport, which is probably a normal function of the endoplasmic reticulum, or in protein synthesis, which takes place on the ribonucleoprotein particles of the reticulum. A function in protein synthesis would be consistent with the appearance of the cytochrome in high concentration in embryonic tissue and mammalian liver cells.

Not only is the behaviour of cytochrome b_5 not consistent with a rôle as terminal oxidase in diapause, but no terminal oxidase other than the ubiquitous cytochrome a has, in fact, been identified in diapausing insects. It is now generally concluded that a quantity of cytochromes b and c sufficient to catalyse the low rate of respiration must be present in diapause tissues, although they are not detectable spectroscopically, and that the respiratory pathway is qualitatively similar to that found in normally developing cells. This theory proposes that cytochrome a is in great excess over cytochromes b and c. Accordingly, it is possible to inactivate a large proportion of the terminal oxidase with cyanide or carbon monoxide while still leaving sufficient to handle the low rate of electron flow from the greatly depleted cytochromes b and c. Some doubt must be entertained, however, about the existence of a typical mitochondrial respiratory system in the persisting embryonic cells of diapause, which are so different in structure and physiology from the differentiated cells into which they develop. It is not even certain that the cyto-chrome a of such cells is located in mitochondria and thus separated from the cytochrome b_5, nor is it clear whether the enzymes of the Krebs cycle are present. In the diapausing egg of the silkworm cytochrome a appears not in the mitochondrial fraction of the cell homogenate, but in the ' lipid-rich particle fraction', probably derived from cell membranes, in which cytochrome b_5 is also located.[14] Other evidence has recently been brought forward of differences in the physical architecture of the cytochrome-containing structures of larval and adult tissues. Thus cytochromes with spectra similar to those designated b and b_5 have been isolated from aqueous extracts of larval insects, whereas, in the adult, cytochromes identified as b and b_5 are so tightly bound to cell structures that drastic treatment with detergents is necessary before their release can be accomplished. Evidence of this kind should make us cautious of accepting any explanation of respiration in embryonic or larval tissue which is based on analogy with the events and pathways of respiration in adult tissue. One may accept the proposition that cytochrome a is the terminal oxidase of diapausing insects, but that the respiration of these insects is the expression of electron flow through a normal mitochondrial electron transport pathway is a horse of a different colour.

Anaerobic mechanisms also play a part in diapause respiration. This could suggest that even the very low energy demands of the insect during suspended development are not fully met by the terminal oxidative pathway, but a more plausible explanation would seem to be that the build up of reduced coenzymes ensuing from the blockage of all anabolic, biosynthetic processes artificially encourages the coupled oxido-reductions of anaerobic energy production. Thus, during diapause in the silkworm egg, all the stored glycogen is converted to glycerol and sorbitol. These two end products may be derived from their respective phosphate esters or be formed more directly as the result of coenzyme-linked reductions.[13] The accumulation of α-glycerophosphate as an end product of anaerobic metabolism has already been shown to be characteristic of insects; sorbitol-6-phosphate is the product of the reduction of fructose-6-phosphate catalysed by an enzyme, known as polyol dehydrogenase, which is active in silkworms, and requires $NADPH_2$ as its coenzyme. The same enzyme is capable of reducing dihydroxyacetone to glycerol. Another NADP-linked enzyme in silkworm eggs reduces glucose directly to sorbitol, and the enzyme which in the normal operation of the Embden-Meyerhof sequence splits fructose-1,6-diphosphate to two triose phosphates (aldolase), also acts on fructose-6-phosphate, producing

glyceraldehyde-3-phosphate and dihydroxyacetone. The diapausing silkworm egg thus possesses a number of enzymes which,
by reducing substrates derived from glycogen, could make possible
the reoxidation of the two coenzymes of cytoplasmic dehydrogenations, and thus encourage energy production by anaerobic

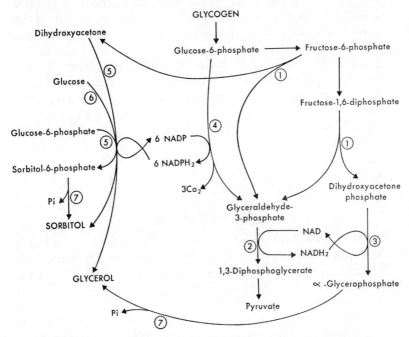

FIG. 7.   Conversion of glycogen to glycerol and sorbitol in
the diapausing silkworm egg.

Catalysts: (1) aldolase, (2) glyceraldehyde-3-phosphate
dehydrogenase, (3) α-glycerophosphate dehydrogenase,
(4) pentose cycle, (5) polyol dehydrogenase a, (6) polyol
dehydrogenase b, (7) phosphomonoesterase.

mechanisms with a consequent by-passing of the terminal oxidative
pathway. The operation of these linked oxidation-reductions is
illustrated in figure 7. The main enzyme responsible for NADH$_2$
production is seen as glyceraldehyde-3-phosphate dehydrogenase,
whereas NADPH$_2$ would be formed mostly by the activity of the
pentose cycle, which will be discussed more fully in a later

M.I.—D

chapter, and which degrades glucose-6-phosphate to glyceraldehyde-3-phosphate and carbon dioxide. It would be expected that the enzymes of the pentose cycle would be prominent in embryonic tissues engaged in biosynthesis. Reoxidation of the two coenzymes has been shown as proceeding by the action of the enzymes mentioned above. Conversion of glycogen to glycerol and sorbitol is thus seen as a more or less accidental result of the continued activity of enzymes present before the onset of diapause. Glycerol accumulates to varying degrees in different diapausing insects, the variation probably reflecting differences in the activities of the reductive enzymes and the degree of their coupling with the oxidative ones. A strange consequence of the accumulation of glycerol, which may appear in remarkably high concentrations in some diapausing insects, is that it causes an appreciable drop in the freezing point of the blood, and thus helps to protect the insect during diapause from the harmful effects of extreme cold.

Other Oxidases

So far in this chapter we have considered only one enzyme which transfers electrons to oxygen—that is, cytochrome oxidase, or cytochrome a. Under normal conditions, cytochrome a is the only oxidase engaged primarily in energy production, and in most instances it is responsible for very nearly all the oxygen consumption. There are, however, a number of enzymes which are capable of using oxygen as a substrate, and since at certain times in the life cycle they may be responsible for an appreciable part of the oxygen consumption some mention should be made of them here.

The flavoprotein dehydrogenases, although normally linked to the cytochrome system, are capable of transferring hydrogen directly to oxygen, and it is conceivable that under some circumstances they might do so *in vivo*. In addition to those mentioned earlier, insects contain a number of other flavoprotein enzymes, such as the D- and L-amino acid oxidases, which catalyse the oxidative deamination of amino acids, and xanthine oxidase, which brings about the oxidation of some purines and pteridines. Since flavoproteins are hydrogen rather than electron donors, the autoxidation of reduced flavoprotein (FPH$_2$) leads to the production of hydrogen peroxide, viz:.

$$FPH_2 + O_2 \longrightarrow FP + H_2O_2.$$

Hydrogen peroxide formed in such reactions may take part in further oxidations, catalysed by haemprotein peroxidases, or by catalase, a special peroxidase which uses hydrogen peroxide as both electron donor and electron acceptor, so that the end products are oxygen and water. All these enzymes, flavoproteins, peroxidases and catalase, are active in insect tissues, but their function is not energy production as such, but rather the special metabolism of the substrates they attack.

One oxidase which is responsible for much of the oxygen consumption at certain stages of insect development is the copper-protein enzyme phenolase. Phenolase catalyses the *ortho*-hydroxylation of phenols or phenol derivatives, such as tyrosine, to form diphenols, and the dehydrogenation of diphenols to form quinones. The activity of this enzyme, or group of enzymes, is of very great importance in the metabolism of insect cuticle, where the quinones formed from derivatives of tyrosine react with the newly formed protein of the cuticle to form stable cross-links, thus ' tanning ' the protein into the hard, dark-coloured, insoluble exocuticle. Moreover, the orthoquinone derivative of tyrosine is itself the precursor of the black pigment melanin, which also contributes to the colouration of insects. Just after moulting, when new cuticle is being hardened, phenolase may be very active, and may be responsible for a significant part of the oxygen consumption. Investigation has shown that at pupation in the blowfly, when an active phenolase coexists with a degenerating larval cytochrome system, up to 85 per cent. of the oxygen uptake is directed to the formation of quinones. Since the quinones formed by phenolase activity may be reduced experimentally by coupling them with NAD-linked dehydrogenases, it has been suggested that phenolase may form part of a natural electron transport system. The involvement of such an electron transport chain in energy production in the cell has never been established, however, and it seems fairly certain that the function of phenolase is confined to the production of quinones, which have important functions in insects unrelated to energy production.

Oxygen Transport

Before leaving the subject of energy production, some mention should be made of the rôle of haemoglobin in insects, small though it is, in facilitating the transport of oxygen to the cells. Nearly all insects rely on the tracheal system for the transport of gaseous oxygen to the immediate vicinity of the cells in which it is used. No oxygen transporting pigment is needed in these circumstances, and none is found. But in three unrelated groups of insects which live in environments poor in oxygen haemoglobin is present either in special cells or in the haemolymph. These insects are the larvae of the botfly at the stage in the life cycle when the maggots live as parasites in the stomach of the horse, and some aquatic Hemiptera and chironomid larvae which live in poorly aerated waters. The iron-porphyrin prosthetic group of haemoglobin is capable of combining reversibly with oxygen without any valence change in the iron atom; that is, haemoglobin is not an electron-transfer pigment, but a transporter of molecular oxygen. The prosthetic group of insect haemoglobin is apparently identical with that of the familiar blood pigment of mammals, but the physical characteristics of the insect pigment differ somewhat from those of its mammalian counterpart.[24] The most important difference is the greater affinity of the insect pigment for oxygen, such that it is fully loaded with oxygen at very low partial pressures. This enables the insect pigment to combine with oxygen at the very low partial pressures present in the surroundings of the insects which contain haemoglobin, and thus aids the entry of oxygen to the cells by eliminating the further drop in partial pressure implicit in a diffusion pathway. Possession of haemoglobin thus enables these insects to make more effective use of the small amounts of oxygen in their environment.

2 : Energy Metabolism

Part 2 : Energy Expenditure

The end result of the complex catabolic pathways considered in the last chapter was the formation of ATP, the link between those energy-yielding processes and the energy-requiring aspects of metabolism to be considered in this chapter. These energy-requiring mechanisms include the biosynthesis of organic molecules from smaller units, the transport of ions across membranes against a concentration gradient, the contraction of muscle, conduction of impulses in nerve, and the production of light. Although it is not the immediate energy source for all these processes, ATP is involved in them all, and, directly or indirectly, the catabolic mechanisms examined in Chapter 1 provide the energy which drives them. Just as the broad outlines of catabolic processes in insects are the same as those in other animals, so the broad outlines of the aspects of energy metabolism to be described in this chapter are the same, but here again we shall encounter differences in detail which may be significantly related to the physiology of insects, and some pathways which seem to be unique.

Biosynthesis

Nucleotides have a key rôle in the metabolic formation of new chemical bonds. The nucleotide may be adenosine triphosphate (when the reactions involve amino acids or fatty acids) uridine triphosphate (when sugars are implicated) or cytidine triphosphate (in the synthesis of compound lipids), while all three of these, plus guanosine triphosphate, take part in the synthesis of ribonucleic acid. Reaction with the nucleotide results in the formation of a nucleoside monophosphate ester and the removal of pyrophosphate. Thus, in the 'activation' of amino acids preceding the formation of peptide bonds in protein synthesis, an aminoacyl adenylate is formed, as follows:

$$R.CHNH_2.COOH+ATP \longrightarrow R.CHNH_2.CO\text{-}AMP+PP.$$

Conjugates of nucleotides such as the aminoacyl adenylates represent the building blocks for the formation of many complex molecules and polymers of high molecular weight. In the case of fatty acid synthesis, the reactive units are thioesters of coenzyme A. These may arise directly from catabolic processes, as was seen in the last chapter, or be formed by the displacement of adenylic acid from an acyl adenylate. The reaction of ATP with acyl groups is reversible, and there is little change in free energy on the formation of an acyl adenylate and pyrophosphate, so it cannot be said that the *energy* of the pyrophosphate linkages of ATP has been used in the synthetic process. In fact, it seems probable that the pyrophosphate formed is immediately hydrolyzed to orthophosphate by the active pyrophosphatases present in most cells. Thus the energy of the pyrophosphate bond seems to be wasted, although combination with a nucleotide is a necessary part of the synthetic process. Perhaps the advantage to the organism in this synthetic pathway is that the hydrolysis of pyrophosphate immediately renders the essential reaction irreversible, by removing one of the reactants which might drive it in the opposite direction. In general, it seems that degradative and synthetic pathways for the same compound in the cell are different. Thus, as we saw in the last chapter, the catabolism of glycogen involves the participation of orthophosphate and the enzyme phosphorylase, whereas glycogen synthesis requires the condensation of uridine diphosphate glucose (UDGP) with the growing glucosyl chain. If glycogen synthesis occurred by a reversal of the phosphorylase reaction, then the direction of metabolism toward degradation or synthesis would be controlled by the concentration of the reactants at any point. For instance, an increase in orthophosphate concentration, such as would result from muscular contraction, could drive the reaction in the direction of synthesis just when catabolism was called for.

The mechanisms of biosynthesis in insects seem to be similar to those of other animals and are probably common to all cells. No further details of them will be given here, therefore, although some specific biosynthetic pathways will be dealt with in later sections on intermediate metabolism. Only one observation on insects which may be of significance in this context need be mentioned. Some insects are known to accumulate in their tissues relatively large concentrations of pyrophosphate and other polyphosphates. Such accumulations are not known elsewhere in the animal kingdom, but have been reported for some bacteria, fungi and algae. Pyrophosphate and metaphosphate have been found in the fat body and male ejaculatory duct of the butterfly, *Deilephila euphorbiae*, while the gut cells and excreta of the wax moth, *Galleria mellonella*, contain polyphosphates of several kinds. It is thought that the accumulation of polyphosphates in the wax moth may be related in some way to the digestion or absorption of the insect's unusual diet of beeswax. It is possible that absorption involves the formation of phospholipids with a consequent production of pyrophosphate, and the excretion of polyphosphates may represent an additional means of eliminating the unwanted metabolite. The status of the biosynthetic mechanisms in these cells which accumulate polyphosphate and their pyrophosphatase activity are unknown, so it is not possible at this stage to comment more precisely on the significance of the findings on pyrophosphate accumulation.

Ion Transport

One of the most characteristic features of a living cell is its ability to move ions against a concentration gradient. Thus most cells maintain within their borders a potassium concentration which is higher and a sodium concentration which is lower than that of the surrounding fluid. This process requires the expenditure of energy, and it is probable that it involves at some stage the dephosphorylation of ATP, but the precise mechanism is unknown. Enzymes or systems which dephosphorylate ATP, and which are specifically activated by either sodium or potassium ions, are known to occur in membranes, and are thought to be part of the ion transport mechanism. Another theory suggests that electron transport systems such as those embedded in the membranes of mitochondria can drive ion transport directly as a consequence of their ability to separate hydrogen and hydroxyl ions on opposite sides of a membrane. Whatever the mechanism, there is no evidence as yet that the cells of insects vary from the general pattern, although it is possible that insect cells do have unusual abilities in ion transport, since they operate in an ionic environment which fluctuates much more violently than does that for vertebrate cells, at least. This is discussed more fully in the next section.

There is one aspect of active transport across membranes which is developed to an unusual degree in insects, and which may, in fact, represent a unique feature of their metabolism. This is the ability of certain insect cells, usually situated in special glands in the rectum, to absorb water against a steep concentration gradient. Conservation of water is of tremendous importance in the economy of most insects, which, because of their small size and active terrestrial existence, are constantly faced with the threat of desiccation. One of the important conservative mechanisms is dehydration of the excreta. Water is absorbed from the gut contents by the rectal glands with such efficiency that the faeces of many species are expelled as dry hard pellets. Unfortunately, nothing is known of the metabolic processes which drive this absorption mechanism.

Conduction in Nerve

The conduction of impulses in nerve is dependent on the nerve cell's ability to transport ions across its plasma membrane. The extrusion of sodium and concentration of potassium by nerve cells, and the presence within the cell of indiffusible anionic groups attached to proteins or other macromolecules leads to the production of an electrical potential across the membrane, the outside being positive in relation to the inside. Conduction involves the depolarization of the membrane at a particular point, the setting up of local currents as a result of the sudden influx of sodium ions and leakage of potassium ions through the now freely permeable depolarized membrane, and the consequent propagation along the fibre of a wave of depolarization. Restoration of excitability involves the reversal of the flow of ions and the renewal of the membrane potential. At junctions between nerve cells or between nerve fibres and muscles a chemical process is believed to take over conduction; a transmitter substance, liberated from one set of endings moves across the junction and causes depolarization of the next nerve cell, initiating a new phase of electrical conduction. According to one view, conduction along nerve fibres is a purely automatic electrical phenomenon once the condition of a polarized membrane is established; another view suggests that changes in membrane permeability are the result of specific biochemical events, that the compound acetylcholine, which is the junctional transmitter substance for many nerves, is released as a result of a stimulus to the nerve cell and by combining with a specific protein receptor causes a change in membrane permeability.

Electrical events in insect nerve seem to be basically similar to those in other animals, but the nerves of insects have one outstanding characteristic in their ability to conduct in ionic surroundings which are quite inhibitory to the nerves of vertebrates. The concentration of sodium in the blood of vertebrates is always higher than the concentration of potassium by a factor of 20 or more, and any considerable increase in the concentration of potassium or decrease in sodium abolishes the ability of the nerves to conduct electrical impulses. Determinations of the ratio of sodium to potassium concentrations in the blood of insects, however, have yielded values ranging from 20 down to 0·1. The ratio may not even be constant from day to day in any one individual. Thus the very high potassium and low sodium concentrations found in the blood of herbivorous insects apparently reflect the concentrations of these ions in the food they eat, and so change with the state of nutrition. Magnesium ions, which are capable of inhibiting vertebrate nerve at quite low concentration, may also be present in the blood of some herbivorous insects in concentrations up to fifty times that found in vertebrates, although it is possible that part of this excess of magnesium may be present in a bound form. A partial explanation of the unusual insensitivity of insect nerves to the ionic environment has been found in the protective action of the cellular and fibrous sheath surrounding the nerves. This sheath had been thought to impose a barrier to the entry of ions to nerves and ganglia, but careful work has established that it is by no means impermeable to ions. On the other hand, the nerve sheath, by virtue of its content of indiffusible anions, does exert an influence on the distribution of ions between the blood and the fluid bathing the nerve fibre itself, the main effect of which is to increase the sodium ion and decrease the chloride ion concentrations of the fluid surrounding the nerve in relation to their concentrations in the blood.[69] This would have an obvious protective effect on the nerves of those insects in which the blood contained high potassium and low sodium concentrations. Possession of a protective sheath, however, does not provide a complete explanation of the insensitivity of insect nerves to their ionic environment, since it has been shown that the nerves of the phasmatid *Carausius morosus* can conduct impulses in a medium completely devoid of sodium ions, and the resting and action potentials of the myocardia of some moths are likewise unaffected by the absence of sodium ions from the surrounding fluid. Since sodium ions carry the current which produces the propagated response, according to the classical view of electrical events in nerve and muscle, it has been suggested that in these insect tissues the rôle of sodium must be assumed by some other ion, perhaps magnesium or calcium. This conclusion is startling, and indicates that studies on insect nerve may be expected to have an important bearing on our eventual understanding of the mechanisms of ion transport and impulse conduction in nerve.

The most widely distributed of the chemical mediators of transmission between nerve cells and between nerve fibres and effector organs is acetylcholine. This compound is responsible for transmission between motor nerves and muscles in vertebrates, acts across some of the junctions in the vertebrate autonomic nervous system, and probably also has a rôle in synaptic transmission in the central nervous system of vertebrates. Although the evidence is indirect, it seems fairly certain that acetylcholine is also the principal conveyor of junctional transmission in insects, and may assume greater importance in the central nervous system of insects than it does in vertebrates.[18] Certainly, the central nervous system of insects contains concentrations of acetylcholine greatly in excess of those found in vertebrate nervous systems. Acetylcholine, diffusing from nerve endings, is rapidly hydrolyzed by the enzyme acetylcholine esterase, which splits the ester to choline and acetic acid, viz.:

$$CH_2.CO.OCH_2.CH_2.\overset{+}{N}.(CH_3)_3 + H_2O$$
$$\text{acetylcholine}$$
$$\longrightarrow CH_3.COOH + HOCH_2.CH_2.\overset{+}{N}.(CH_3)_3$$
$$\text{acetic acid} \qquad\qquad \text{choline}$$

The rapid hydrolysis of acetylcholine after the passage of an impulse across a synapse makes possible the restoration of the nerve cell membrane to its resting condition; inhibition of the hydrolyzing enzyme leads to repeated discharges from a single stimulus, and the eventual blockage of transmission. Since the majority of the more successful recent insecticides are inhibitors of acetylcholine esterase, a great deal of attention has been devoted to the enzyme, and its properties are well documented. Its activity in the central nervous system of insects is very high. Nervous tissue also contains a system for the resynthesis of acetylcholine. This requires the preliminary formation of acetyl-coenzyme A in a reaction which involves ATP,

$$\text{acetate} + CoA + ATP \longrightarrow \text{acetyl-CoA} + \text{adenylic acid} + \text{pyrophosphate},$$

followed by the transfer of the acetyl group to choline,

$$\text{choline} + \text{acetyl-CoA} \longrightarrow \text{acetylcholine} + CoA.$$

Although acetylcholine is widely distributed in the nervous systems of animals it is not the only mediator of synaptic or neuromuscular transmission. Both adrenalin and noradrenalin, which is the transmitter substance of the postganglionic section of the mammalian sympathetic nervous system, are known to occur in insects, and may have a function in transmission, but no one has yet succeeded in identifying adrenergic junctions in insects. Other insect metabolites thought to be involved in the physiology of nerve are 5-hydroxytryptamine (serotonin) and γ-aminobutyric acid. These compounds have a wide distribution among invertebrate and vertebrate animals, but their precise rôle in nerve transmission has not been worked out. It has been suggested that they may have a function in transmission in the central nervous system or in mediating the action of inhibitory fibres. The concentration of these substances in the brains of vertebrate animals supports such conclusions, but very little is known of their distribution in the insect nervous system and the data are too few to permit speculations about their action in the nervous systems of these animals.

The functioning of the nervous system of insects is modified by the action of hormones released into the haemolymph, just as it is in vertebrates, although the chemical identity of the insect nerve hormones has not been established. It is also known that insects which are subjected to physical stress secrete into their blood substances which have pronounced pharmacological and even lethal effects when injected into healthy insects. The blood of insects poisoned with DDT, which induces hyperactivity followed by prostration, contains a substance with similar effects. The corpora cardiaca are probably the major source of hormones of this type, but other tissues, such as the pericardial cells and accessory glands of the reproductive system, have been shown to be involved. The metabolism of the insect nerve hormones is discussed further in the section dealing with the metabolism of tryptophan, from which some, at least, seem to be derived.

Some of the nerve hormones of insects are apparently identical with, or closely related to, those of vertebrates, since extracts of the corpora cardiaca of insects have dynamic effects on vertebrate smooth muscle preparations. Moreover, insects exploit their capacity to synthesize such compounds by concentrating them in venom glands. Among the agents in insect venoms which produce general systemic effects on both invertebrate and vertebrate victims are acetylcholine, histamine and serotonin.

Very little can be said about the metabolic mechanisms associated with the higher integrative functions of the central nervous system, such as the storage of information and its retrieval in memory, as this represents one of the major unsolved fields in biology. Some work on the relationships between behaviour and the physiology of the nervous system has already been done in insects, however, and it is to be expected that when this field does finally open up to intense study the insects, with their exaggerated development of inherent behaviour patterns, may prove to be rewarding objects of attention.

Contraction in Muscle

The major user of metabolic energy in mobile animals is muscle, and here it seems certain that ATP is the immediate source of the energy for contraction. Early searchers for the energy sources of muscular work, concentrating on vertebrate muscle, established that glycogen was broken down to lactic acid during contraction and equated this process energetically with the mechanical work done. Later it was found that glycolysis could be completely prevented by treating the muscle with iodoacetate and thus inhibiting the glyceraldehyde-3-phosphate dehydrogenase, but that such muscles were still able to perform a limited number of contractions. Orthophosphate was found to accumulate during contraction in muscles poisoned with iodoacetate. The source of this phosphate, the ' phosphagen ', was identified as creatine phosphate, which became the next candidate to be considered the energy source of muscle. When the widespread importance of ATP in metabolic energy relations was established, it was realized that ATP was probably the immediate energy source, but that it was rapidly reformed by the transfer of phosphate from creatine phosphate by the enzyme phosphocreatine kinase, which is active in vertebrate muscle. Finally, by the use of a specific inhibitor for the kinase, the direct demonstration of the dephosphorylation of ATP in an early phase of muscle contraction, a goal which had eluded investigators for many years, was achieved.

One finds in muscle a close physical and functional relationship between the mitochondria which produce ATP and the contractile fibrils which use it. A muscle cell, or fibre, is normally extremely elongated and spindle shaped, and runs the whole length of the muscle. Lying within the sarcoplasm are a number of fibrils, also continuous throughout the entire length, numerous mitochondria dispersed between the fibrils and usually in close contact with them, and a smooth endoplasmic reticulum. Perhaps the most advanced development of the relationship between mitochondria and fibrils is found in the flight muscles of some of the higher orders of insects (Diptera, Hymenoptera, Coleoptera and some Hemiptera). These so-called ' fibrillar ' flight muscles, lying within the hard box of the thorax, are distinguished by a complete absence of the protective connective tissue sheath which surrounds the fibres of almost all mammalian muscle and is also found in reduced amounts in some insect muscles. Flight muscle fibres are large in diameter in relation to their length, and since the investing membrane is thin and transparent, the structural units of the muscle appear to be the fibrils rather than the fibres. The fibrils, which are of large diameter in comparison with mammalian fibrils, are arranged in parallel columns between which are packed large numbers of mitochondria, which are also two or three times larger than those encountered in any other muscle. The mitochondria, or sarcosomes, occupy almost all the space between the fibrils, being so tightly packed that they are mostly distorted from the more usual semi-spherical shape. Only a few elements of the endoplasmic reticulum are present. We have already seen that these fibrillar muscles exhibit the most perfect development of the aerobic mechanisms for linking carbohydrate catabolism with ATP production, the active α-glycerophosphate cycle for feeding electrons into the mitochondria replacing the anaerobic mechanisms found in most mammalian muscle.

As far as is known, all insect muscles are striated, unlike the condition in vertebrates, where the voluntary, or somatic, muscles are striated, and the involuntary, or visceral, muscles are smooth. In striated muscle the fibrils are divided into segments, called sarcomeres, by a regular succession of transverse septa, the Z lines. The septa of all the fibrils in any one fibre are usually in register, and thus appear as dark striations running across the fibre. Within each sarcomere is a central denser zone, which is bi-refringent and is called the A (anisotropic) band. These alternate with lighter areas, each of which is bisected by the Z line, known as I (isotropic) bands (fig. 8). The fine structure of the fibril has been established by electron microscopy of thin longitudinal and transverse sections of muscle fibres, and confirmed by X-ray analysis. Each sarcomere contains a double array of inter-digitating filaments. The thicker filaments, which occupy the A band, apparently have no connection with the Z discs. Thinner filaments are attached to the Z discs, but end short of the centre of the sarcomere, although a fine elastic connection is believed to join opposing ends of thin filaments in this region. Regular cross bridges occur between the two sets of filaments. It is the presence of the thick filaments which gives the A band its greater protein

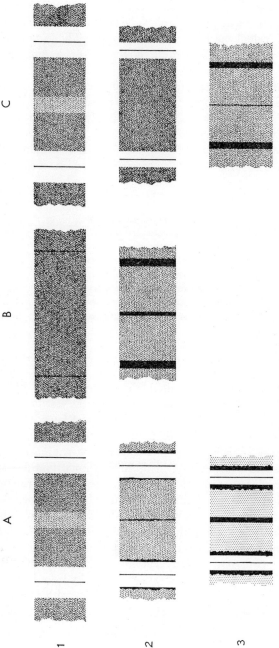

Fig. 8. Contraction sequences in individual sarcomeres of (A) locust leg muscle, (B) blowfly flight muscle and (C) rabbit leg muscle: (1) uncontracted, (2) partially contracted, (3) contracted to 70 per cent. of rest length.

density, and renders it birefringent. The absence of thin filaments from the centre of the sarcomere explains the lighter appearance of this region, called the H (for ' helle ') zone. The arrangement of filaments within the sarcomere is shown diagrammatically in figure 9.

Study on the biochemistry of the contraction process received its first great stimulus from the discovery that myosin, the protein extracted from muscle by salt solution, catalysed the hydrolysis of the terminal phosphate group of ATP, and, when precipitated in the form of a thread, would ' contract ' on the addition of ATP. Myosin thus seemed to be the transducer which converted the

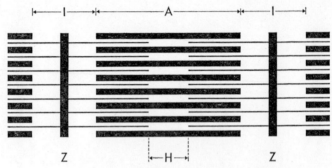

FIG. 9.   Diagram of the fine structure of a sarcomere.

chemical energy of the terminal phosphate bond of ATP into mechanical work. Much patient work over the last twenty years had led to the accumulation of a great mass of knowledge of the physico-chemical properties of myosin, and its interaction with ATP, but the basic molecular mechanism of the energy transduction remains a mystery. One of the first important discoveries was that two different proteins could be separated from the myosin of the earlier workers. The name ' myosin ' was retained for one of these, although it is usually distinguished by the terms ' myosin A ' or ' L-myosin ', while the other was called ' actin '. Neither of these proteins is itself contractile, but a stoichiometric combination of the two, now called ' actomyosin ' or ' myosin B ', is. Myosin A has the enzymatic site for the hydrolysis of ATP. Actin exists as a globular protein in solution, with one mole of ATP tightly bound to each mole of protein. These globular molecules can be induced to polymerize into long fibres which form very viscous solutions. The bound ATP is dephosphorylated in this process, and so the fibrous actin contains tightly bound ADP. Thus ATP is involved both in the formation of the filamentous molecular structure of muscle as well as in driving the contraction process.

A third protein extracted from the contractile apparatus is called ' tropomyosin '. This seems to have a minor rôle in most striated muscle, but a closely related protein is a major constituent of the tonic smooth muscle of some molluscs, where it occurs in isolated filaments, and is apparently responsible for the ability of these muscles to ' set ' in the contracted state, thus maintaining tension for long periods with little expenditure of energy.

More recent work has paid attention to an additional factor from outside the fibril which influences the performance of extracted proteins or contraction models *in vitro*. This is the so-called ' relaxing factor ', which inhibits the ATPase activity of actomyosin, and under appropriate conditions prevents contraction or causes relaxation of muscle models. The relaxing factor, which itself is inhibited by calcium ions, has been identified with the microsomal fraction of muscle, that is, with the minute fragments of the endoplasmic reticulum of the disrupted muscle cells. According to current ideas of the probable sequence of events, all the ATP of muscle in the relaxed state may be bound to the relaxing factor. Calcium ions, dislodged from the cell's membrane system by the exciting current, may disrupt this association, thus releasing ATP for combination with the contractile apparatus. It is believed that the phosphagen and phosphokinase system, which itself can act as a relaxing factor in *in vitro* models, has an important early rôle. Perhaps the enzyme removes ADP from the contracted protein, achieves its immediate phosphorylation by the phosphagen, and segregates it from the contractile apparatus by combining it with the relaxing factor.

Observations on changes in the distribution of proteins within the sarcomere during contraction of isolated myofibrils have revealed that in vertebrate myofibrils the A bands appear not to shorten during contraction. As the Z discs move toward one another the I bands gradually disappear, until finally the Z discs impinge on the ends of the A bands (fig. 8). Contraction beyond

M.I.—E

this point is accompanied by the formation of dense areas in the Z region and also in the centre of the sarcomere. These are referred to as contraction bands, and are named C_z and C_m respectively. This sequence of events suggests that the filaments of the sarcomere do not themselves contract, but that they slide relative to one another, the thin filaments being drawn in between the thick filaments until finally the Z discs impinge on the ends of the thick filaments. Continuation of the same process beyond this point results in the crumpling up of the ends of the thick filaments to form the C_z bands, and of the inner ends of the thin filaments to form the C_m bands. Moreover, it has been established by differentially dissolving out the muscle components that the thick filaments of rabbit muscle, at least, are composed of myosin, and the thin filaments of actin plus tropomyosin. Thus the actomyosin which formed the basis of many earlier models of contraction, may to some degree be an artefact of extraction, the component proteins being separated in different filaments in muscle. According to this view of contraction, the combination of ATP with the myosin of the thick filaments, probably on the bridges which seem to form regularly spaced projections from the thick filaments, sets up forces which cause the thick and thin filaments to move past one another. Various plausible theories have been put forward to account for this action, but need not be entered into here.

Turning now from the consideration of the metabolism of muscle in general to the special biochemistry of insect muscle, we find that the phosphagen of insects is arginine phosphate, as it is in many other invertebrates. At one time it was though that this difference in phosphagens expressed a constant biochemical difference between vertebrate and invertebrate, but now it is known that whereas vertebrates seem to rely on creatine phosphate exclusively, invertebrates contain a number of substituted guanidyl compounds which act as phosphagens, including both creatine and arginine phosphates. Of these, only arginine phosphate has been found in insects. It occurs in flight muscle in concentrations much lower than the usual phosphagen content of vertebrate muscle, suggesting that its rôle may be less crucial in the functioning of the insect muscle. Perhaps the very efficient aerobic ATP production of flight muscle reduces the need for an intermediate energy store. Insect muscle also contains an arginine phosphokinase, which catalyses the specific transfer of a phosphate group from the phosphagen to ADP.

The proteins of the contractile apparatus of insect muscle seem to be closely related to those of vertebrates.[46, 24] Although myosin A cannot be isolated directly from insect muscle, it can be separated from insect actomyosin. Its enzymatic and physicochemical characteristics are similar to those of its vertebrate counterpart, and the same can be said for insect actin. However, actomyosins extracted directly from various insect muscles invariably have a higher viscosity and more intense birefringence of flow, indicating a more pronounced fibrous structure, than vertebrate actomyosins isolated in the same way.

Structurally, also, insect muscle seems very akin to vertebrate striated muscle. The same double array of filaments has been demonstrated, and although there are rather more thin filaments in relation to the number of thick filaments than in mammalian muscle, it might seem that the same contraction mechanism could be expected. The myofibrils of indirect flight muscle present a rather unusual appearance in that at rest length I bands are either not visible or are extremely reduced in size, the A bands extending to the immediate vicinity of the Z discs. Contraction in these muscles results in the immediate appearance of the contraction band pattern (fig. 8), and I bands can only be demonstrated by stretching the muscle beyond rest length.[30] This difference, however, is thought to be merely an adaptation to the normal physiological activity of the muscle. The two opposing sets of indirect flight muscles shorten by only one to two per cent. in effecting wing movements. Under these circumstances, longer A bands, with a more extensive overlap of thick and thin filaments, might be expected to produce a more powerful contraction, whereas in muscles which normally shorten by much greater amounts, as do many vertebrate muscles, longer A bands might impede movement by entanglement with the Z discs.

Since the endoplasmic reticulum is so reduced in fibrillar flight muscle, one wonders about the production of relaxing factor in such muscles. Recent electron microscope studies have shown that although one component of the endoplasmic reticulum which is thought to be important in impulse conduction is present in fibrillar muscle, the other component, which is concerned with relaxation, is entirely absent. It may be significant that isolated myofibrils from fibrillar flight muscle have been found to relax spontaneously only when they are in contact with mitochondria.[31] Perhaps the mitochondria of this muscle produce the relaxing factor.

Although the proteins of the contractile apparatus of insect muscle are similar to those of vertebrates, their distribution within the sarcomere may be different. Attempts to extract the ' A substance ', that is, the material of the thick filaments, of insect muscle have invariably brought into solution a protein of the actomyosin type. Although it is impossible to be certain that no material has dissolved from the thin filaments, this result suggests that the thick filaments of insect muscle are not composed of myosin alone, but contain the contractile complex actomyosin. Such a difference in distribution of proteins would make more credible the repeated observations of the histologists of fifty or more years ago that the A bands of insect muscle shorten during contraction. A recent study of contraction in isolated myofibrils of locust leg muscle has confirmed these observations, demonstrating a reduction in length of both A and I bands as the sarcomere shortens. Furthermore, changes in protein density within the A band suggest that shortening is the result of *contraction* of the thick filaments.[25] These changes are the development of dense regions at the outer edges and in the middle of the A band, which seem to correspond with C_z and C_m bands, and a decrease in protein density between these areas (fig. 8). Such contraction bands develop in the presence of I bands. Shortening of the A band, and an A substance composed of actomyosin, have also been reported in the marine arthropod *Limulus*, so it is possible that a contraction mechanism involving coiling of the thick filaments instead of, or as well as, relative sliding of the two sets of filaments is characteristic of all arthropod muscle. It is still too early to say just what the significance of these differences is. One would expect the basic molecular mechanism of energy transduction in muscle to be the same thoughout the animal kingdom, and, in fact, very recent electron microscope studies have cast some doubt on the sliding filament concept, even as an explanation of contraction in vertebrate muscle. Perhaps some degree of coiling of myofilaments, comparable with the intramolecular synaeresis of actomyosin models, occurs in all muscle, arthropod muscle being merely specially suited to observation of the phenomenon by the light microscope. More exact comparisons will be needed before any common model of contraction, valid for striated muscle of any origin, can be proposed.

One other aspect of muscle metabolism in which studies on insect muscle have revealed metabolic changes which run counter to the vertebrate pattern remains to be discussed. Vertebrate muscle contains a very active adenylic acid deaminase which removes the amino group from the purine ring of adenylic acid, to produce inosinic acid. This enzyme seems to have an active metabolic rôle in muscle, as it has been shown that there is a rapid turnover of the amino nitrogen of muscle adenylate during activity. Reamination of inosinic acid is achieved by a pathway which involves aspartic acid as an amino donor. No adenylic acid deaminase has been found in insect muscle, nor in the muscle of any invertebrate so far examined. At the moment this fact expresses no more than a biological curiosity, since the function of the deaminase and the significance of the rapid amino turnover in vertebrate muscle are unknown, but it serves as a further illustration of the need for comparative studies as a preliminary to the formulation of general conclusions on metabolic function.

Light Production

The ability to produce light is shared by a very diverse collection of organisms, including bacteria, fungi, numerous invertebrate animals, and some vertebrates. In all such organisms the luminescent reaction involves the oxidation by molecular oxygen of a substrate which is referred to as luciferin, the reaction being catalysed by an enzyme called luciferase. Presumably oxidation leads to the production of an excited intermediate which decays to the ground state with the emission of energy in the form of light. Luciferins from different organisms differ widely in structure, but all are highly fluorescent. Since bioluminescence is such a widespread phenomenon it might be supposed that it is the product of a process that arose very early in organic evolution. It has been suggested, in fact, that its value lay in the rapid removal of oxygen in the predominantly anaerobic environment at the dawn of evolution. The persistence of bioluminescence in many organisms may be hard to understand, but in most luminescent insects light production has an obvious evolutionary value as a lure for prey or an attractant of one sex for the other.

The best known and brightest lights of the insect world are the fireflies, most which are lampyrid or elaterid beetles. These insects produce intermittent flashes of light of various colours from groups of organs, known as lanterns, which may be situated on almost any part of the body. Since fireflies congregate in large numbers, and since all the individuals in any tree may synchronize their flashes, they are capable of spectacular and beautiful effects.

The molecular mechanism of light production has been studied most intensively in the North American firefly, *Photinus pyralis*, which emits bright flashes of greenish yellow light from lanterns near the tip of the abdomen.[45] The *Photinus* luminescent system, which is illustrated in figure 10, is unusual in that it requires ATP as well as luciferin, oxygen and luciferase. ATP first combines

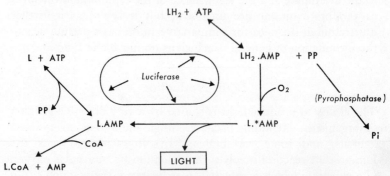

FIG. 10.   Light production in the firefly.

LH_2 = luciferin;   L = dehydro-luciferin;   L*AMP = excited form of dehydro-adenyl-luciferin;   PP = pyrophosphate; P_i = orthophosphate.

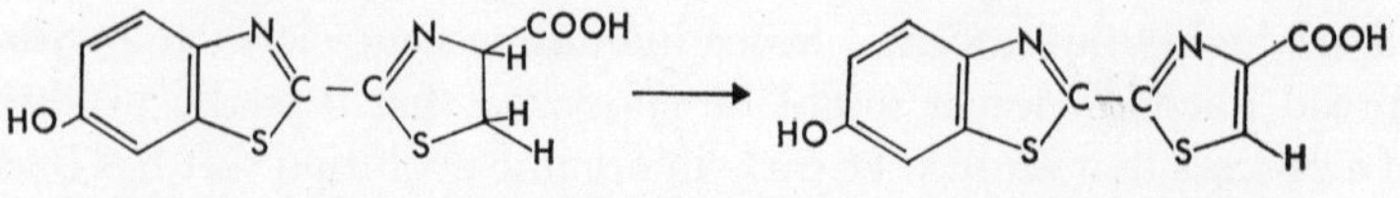

FIG. 11.   Oxidation of firefly luciferin to dehydro-luciferin.

with luciferin in a dark anaerobic reaction which yeilds adenyl-luciferin and pyrophosphate. Adenyl-luciferin then becomes the substrate for oxidation and light production. The enzyme luciferase catalyses both the reaction with ATP and the oxidation. Firefly luciferin has been isolated in a pure state, and its chemical structure, shown in figure 11, has been confirmed by total synthesis. Combination with adenylic acid occurs through the carboxyl group. The compound can be obtained in two stereo-isomers, of which only the D(−) form is oxidized by luciferase with the production of light. The L(+) form binds to the enzyme but is not oxidized. The mechanism of oxidation and the details of the excitation process are still not understood. The final oxidized product, dehydro-luciferin, has the structure shown in figure 11, and it is known that hydrogen peroxide is not an end product, so it has been suggested that the initial process is the formation of an organic hydroperoxide, which decomposes to leave an atom of oxygen attached to the intermediate compound. At alkaline pH's, one quantum of light (57 kcal. at the wave length of maximum emission) is released for every mole of luciferin consumed. The oxidation thus releases a large amount of energy in one step, and is obviously quite distinct from the usual oxidation process of respiration, where electrons flow through a series of redox systems, releasing a small amount of energy at each step. If the pH of the firefly luminescent system is lowered, the intensity of the yellow-green light decreases and the colour changes finally to a dull brick-orange glow, indicating that the kind of excitation is dependent on the state of ionization of the luciferin-luciferase complex. Moreover, at the lower pH some molecules of luciferin fail to emit light on oxidation, and the quantum yield falls below one.

In the *in vitro* system, the flash of light which results when one of the reactants, for example ATP, is added to the otherwise complete system fades rapidly. This is because dehydro-adenyl-luciferin remains tightly bound to the enzyme, and inhibits further light production, even when an excess of luciferin and ATP is present. This inhibition may be lifted in two ways. The addition of pyrophosphate causes a rise in light intensity, because it reacts with the bound dehydro-adenyl-luciferin to form free dehydro-luciferin and ATP. Conversely the enzyme pyrophosphatase inhibits light production by removing the pyrophosphate formed in the initial reaction. The addition of pyrophosphate does not restore oxidation at the maximum rate, however, since the increase in pyrophosphate concentration tends to reverse the initial combination of luciferin and ATP (fig. 10). Coenzyme A also reverses the inhibition by forming free dehydro-luciferyl-coenzyme A and adenylic acid. Physiological light production may depend on the intervention of one, or perhaps both of these mechanisms. It is known that light emission in the firefly is under nervous control, and it has been suggested that pyrophosphate formed in the resynthesis of acetylcholine, which in turn is stimulated by acetylcholine *breakdown* at the nerve endings, may set off the flash by lifting the inhibition of the luciferase. Although firefly lanterns contain an active pyrophosphatase, the enzyme may not compete successfully with the luminescent system for the pyrophosphate formed. Reformation of luciferin, which is presumably achieved by reduction of the dehydro-luciferin formed in the luminescent reaction, has not been investigated.

Most luminescent organisms produce blue light, with a relatively greater energy output than that of the firefly. The higher energy production requires a larger difference in redox potential between the substrate to be oxidized and oxygen, and many luminescent systems use such highly reduced substrates as the pyridine nucleotides as luciferins. Only one organism is known to produce red light. This is the so-called railroad worm, the larva, or larviform female of a tropical beetle, which carries a red light on its head, and a series of yellow-green spots along both sides. Neither the structures nor the mechanisms of oxidation of the luciferins of this beetle are known.

3 : Carbohydrate Metabolism

The class of compounds of organic origin known as carbohydrates includes the water-soluble, polyhydroxy sugars, and a number of their derivatives. Although carbon, hydrogen and oxygen are the main constituents of the carbohydrates, as the name implies, some members of the group include nitrogen or sulphur atoms in their structure. The carbohydrates are conveniently divided into the single sugars, or monosaccharides, of which the six-carbon hexoses and the five-carbon pentoses are the most important, the oligosaccharides, which consist structurally of a number of sugars linked together through glycosidic bonds, which involve the condensation of the reducing end of one sugar with an hydroxyl group of another, and the polysaccharides, which are high-molecular-weight polymers of many sugar units in glycosidic linkage. Some aspects of carbohydrate metabolism have already been considered in the chapter on energy production; this chapter will deal more generally with the transformations and physiological importance of the carbohydrates.

Most animals require in their diet not only a number of organic molecules (vitamins and essential amino acids) which they are unable to synthesize themselves, but also a reasonably balanced proportion of the three major classes of foodstuffs, carbohydrates, fats and proteins. Although mechanisms for the interconversion of these three classes are to be found in most, if not all, animals, the pathways are not active enough to provide for maximum growth unless all three are provided in the diet. Many insects live and grow on a remarkably restricted diet. The clothes moth may eat only protein, the wax moth can live on beeswax, and many insects, such as those which feed on flour, or dead wood, or the nectar of flowers, have a diet that is abnormally rich in carbohydrate. Even in these cases the growth may be stimulated by providing a more balanced diet—it is well known that clothes moths grow best on contaminated wool, and that wax moths eat much debris in the hive as well as the comb wax—but nevertheless it is clear that the metabolism of these species must be highly specialized for carrying out the necessary conversions from their restricted diet. It is not surprising that several insects living on a diet rich in carbohydrate are so adapted to this mode of life that they are unable to survive in the absence of carbohydrate. The blowfly *Calliphora* is an outstanding example of such metabolic specialization. Although as larvae blowflies feed on a diet rich in protein, and store up large quantities of fat, which survive pupation, as adults they are completely dependent on a dietary supply of carbohydrate and do not survive long in its absence.

The Monosaccharides

Hexoses and their derivatives

Glucose, which is the physiologically important blood sugar of vertebrates, is usually only a minor constituent of insect blood, and there is no evidence of any regulatory mechanism controlling its concentration. It has been found in appreciable amounts in the blood of some flies, and, not unexpectedly, reaches very high concentrations (around 3 gm. per 100 ml.) in the blood of worker bees engaged in honey production. In the majority of insects, however, glucose is present in very low concentration in the blood, the major blood sugar being the disaccharide trehalose, the metabolism of which will be discussed in a later section. Fructose, also, is a minor constituent of the blood of most insects, but is present in high concentration in the blood of the honeybee, and is the major blood sugar of the larvae of the botfly, *Gasterophilus*. The presence of fructose in the honeybee, which is engaged in the conversion of the sucrose of nectar into the glucose and fructose of honey, is understandable, but the significance of the high fructose content of *Gasterophilus* blood is unknown. It is probable that in insects, as in other animals, fructose is the main energy source for the spermatozoa, since in one species, at least, fructose is rapidly metabolized in the ejaculated semen.

Formation and excretion of glucosides is an important method in insects for the detoxication of phenols and other reactive and potentially harmful molecules.[65] Phenols fed to or injected into insects of several orders are excreted in the form of β-glucosides. In mammals the analogous detoxication process involves conjugation with glucuronic acid. Some insects may also form glucuronides, but formation of glucosides is by far the most important mechanism. A number of β-glucosides are also known to occur naturally in insects, and several of them are apparently detoxication products of aromatic molecules absorbed from the plant diet. They include a number of plant pigments, such as anthraquinones, anthocyanins, flavones and the so-called ' aphins ', which are incorporated into the insect body as part of its colouration. They may be absorbed as glucosides, or detoxified by conjugation with glucose after entering the insect's body. Glucoside formation in insects, as in other animals, involves the participation of the nucleotide uridine triphosphate (UTP), and proceeds according to the following reaction sequence:

Glucose-1-phosphate+UTP $\longrightarrow$ uridine diphosphate glucose (UDPG)
+pyrophosphate

Phenol+UDPG $\longrightarrow$ phenyl-glucoside+UDP

The fat body is the site of such glucoside formation. Uridine diphosphate derivatives of several carbohydrates occur in appreciable amounts in the haemolymph of insects.

Since the formation of β-glucosides is a common reaction in plants as well as insects, most plant-feeding animals secrete active β-glucosidases in their digestive tracts. Insects are no exception to this rule, and the crop contents of locusts, in particular, are rich in this enzyme. β-Glucosidases occur in many insect tissues, however, and probably have a general function in degrading oligosaccharides with β linkages. Apart from this general rôle, several instances are known in which β-glucosidases have a special function of considerable physiological significance. The right colleterial glands of several species of cockroach produce β-glucosidases, which mix with the products of the left colleterial glands during secretion of the ootheca. The products of the left colleterial gland are firstly, the β-glucoside of the *ortho*-diphenol protocatechuic acid, secondly, the enzyme phenolase, and thirdly, the protein from which the ootheca is constructed. On mixture of the two secretions, the β-glucosidase of the right colleterial gland splits the glucosidic bond, releasing the diphenol, which is oxidized by the phenolase to the corresponding quinone, and this, in turn, reacts with the protein, tanning it to the hardened final product.

Glucosidases also play a part in producing some of the defensive secretions of insects. The cockroach, *Diploptera punctata*, which secretes a solution of *para*-quinones as a means of defence, has a β-glucosidase in the defensive glands, and it is assumed that the mechanism of release of the quinones involves the hydrolysis of phenyl glucosides, as in the tanning of the cockroach ootheca.[59] A variant of this process may be responsible for part of the defensive system of larvae and adults of certain zygaenid moths which are repugnant to birds and other vertebrates. The crushed tissues of these insects emit hydrogen cyanide, and the haemolymph, which may be exuded from special bleeding areas, also contains cyanide. It seems probable that the cyanide is a product of the hydrolysis by a β-glucosidase of a cyanogenic glucoside absorbed from the food plant, although there is no certainty of this, since the insects contain cyanide even when reared on plants not known to contain cyanogenic glucosides. The insect itself is apparently immune to the effects of cyanide, but by what means is not known. These cyanide-producing moths harbour a number of insect parasites which also seem to be immune to the poison. Some explanation of the parasites' resistance to cyanide may be found in the presence in their tissues of the enzyme rhodanese, which detoxifies cyanide by the addition of sulphur from thiosulphate, itself probably an end product of cysteine metabolism.

The amino sugar glucosamine and its acetylated derivative *N*-acetylglucosamine have an important metabolic rôle in insects, since they are intermediates in the synthesis of the polysaccharide component of the cuticle, chitin. Their metabolism is discussed along with that of chitin in a later section of this chapter.

Pathways for the interconversion and catabolism of the hexoses have been dealt with in Chapter 1, and are summarized in figure 1. A number of the intermediates in these pathways may have special physiological functions in insects not connected with energy production. Several of the organic acids of the citric acid cycle are present in unusually high concentration in the blood of insects, and in some species may account for half the total anion of the blood.[77] Citrate, in particular, has been demonstrated in several species, but there are reports also of high concentrations of succinate, malate, fumarate and α-ketoglutarate. It has already been suggested that the accumulation of such intermediates may have some significance in anaerobic energy production in the larvae of *Gasterophilus*, in which succinate and malate are the major organic acids. Another possible explanation of the presence of high concentrations of intermediates would be the existence of an active glyoxylate cycle converting fat to carbohydrate, but although it appears that this cycle may play some part in insect metabolism (see Chapter 4), it seems not to be active at the time when citrate and other acids are accumulated. In fact, no adequate explanation has yet been put forward for the occurrence of unusual amounts of the acid intermediates in the blood of insects of many different habits.

Calcium citrate is present in a special gland of the preying mantis, the secretion of which is added to that of the colleterial gland at the time of egg laying. The function of the citrate is not known, but it is thought that it may play a part in the coagulation or hardening of the protein secreted by the colleterial gland as it is formed into the papery mantid ootheca. The calcium salt of another organic acid may serve the same function in the American cockroach. The left colleterial gland of this species secretes calcium oxalate, which eventually appears as crystals in the hardened ootheca. Oxalic acid, which is a typical plant product, is usually not accumulated by animals, although it may be excreted as a degradation product of ascorbic acid. It can be derived metabolically from glyoxylic acid, or possibly from methyl glyoxal, which is produced from lactic acid by the action of the enzyme glyoxylase.

$$\begin{array}{ccccccc}
\text{COOH} & & \text{CHO} & & \text{COOH} & & \text{CHO} \\
| & \xrightarrow{-H_2O} & | & \dashrightarrow & | & \longleftarrow\text{- - - -} & | \\
\text{HCOH} & & \text{C}{=}\text{O} & & \text{COOH} & & \text{COOH} \\
| & & | & & & & \\
\text{CH}_3 & & \text{CH}_3 & & & & \\
\text{lactic acid} & & \text{methyl glyoxal} & & \text{oxalic acid} & & \text{glyoxylic acid}
\end{array}$$

Glyoxylase is known to occur in insects, but whether or not it is involved in a pathway of oxalic acid synthesis has not been determined.

Two acid derivatives of the hexoses, ascorbic acid and gluconic acid, have special functions in insects, while a third acid derivative, glucuronic acid, is known to be a constituent of insect polysaccharides.

$$
\begin{array}{ccc}
\begin{array}{l}
O{=}C\!-\!\rule{0pt}{0pt}\\
\;\;\;|\\
HOC\\
\;\;\;\|\quad O\\
HOC\\
\;\;\;|\\
HC\!-\!\rule{0pt}{0pt}\\
\;\;\;|\\
HOCH\\
\;\;\;|\\
CH_2OH
\end{array}
&
\begin{array}{l}
COOH\\
|\\
HCOH\\
|\\
HOCH\\
|\\
HCOH\\
|\\
HCOH\\
|\\
CH_2OH
\end{array}
&
\begin{array}{l}
CHO\\
|\\
HCOH\\
|\\
HOCH\\
|\\
HCOH\\
|\\
HCOH\\
|\\
COOH
\end{array}\\
\text{ascorbic acid} & \text{gluconic acid} & \text{glucuronic acid}
\end{array}
$$

Many insects have no need for ascorbic acid (vitamin C) in the diet, but it has been shown to be an essential nutrient for several phytophagous species. In one cockroach, at least, ascorbic acid is made by intracellular symbiotes, and it may be that insect tissues, in general, are incapable of synthesizing the vitamin, and only those that harbour symbiotic micro-organisms are independent of a dietary supply. Mannose, and, less effectively, other hexoses have been shown to be precursors of ascorbic acid in insects, but the details of the synthetic pathway are unknown. Ascorbic acid has been shown to activate the enzyme phenolase in insects, and has also been identified as an inhibitor of pigment formation by the same enzyme. It may exert a general regulatory effect, by mechanisms as yet unknown, on the metabolism of phenolic compounds derived from tyrosine (see Chapter 6).

The direct oxidation of glucose to gluconic acid is a reaction characteristic of a number of fungi. The enzyme responsible is a flavoprotein, and like other flavoproteins forms hydrogen peroxide as a reaction product. A similar enzyme is present in honey, where the hydrogen peroxide it produces has been identified as the bacteriostatic substance of honey, called ' inhibine ' before its chemical nature was identified.[72] Dilution of honey increases the activity of the enzyme, which itself is apparently inhibited by its reaction product, hydrogen peroxide. The presence of this enzyme along with high concentrations of its substrate thus provides honey with a bactericidal system which is semi-permanent and self-regulating. As far as is known, the glucose oxidase of honey is not a fungal enzyme, but is secreted along with the invertase of honey by the pharyngeal glands of the worker bee.

Polyhydric alcohols are formed by the reduction of sugars. Mention has already been made of the probable significance of such reductions in diapause metabolism and anaerobic energy production. An enzyme in the blood of the silkworm catalyses the reduction of glucose-6-phosphate to sorbitol-6-phosphate, and another is responsible for the reduction of monosaccharides of three, four, or five carbon atoms to their corresponding alcohols. Similar activity has been found in the diapausing egg of the silkworm, which also contains an enzyme capable of reducing glucose directly to sorbitol. All these enzymes transfer electrons from $NADPH_2$, and establish equilibria which favour reduction of the sugar rather than oxidation of the alcohol.

Other Monosaccharides

The main pathway for the interconversion of the sugars is the pentose cycle,[12] the reactions of which are shown in figure 12. The enzymes of the pentose cycle are found in the soluble fraction of insect cells. The first two reactions of the cycle are dehydrogenations in which NADP is the electron acceptor. Since the group transfer reactions catalysed by the enzymes transaldolase and transketolase can use several sugars both as group donors or acceptors, they provide an effective mechanism for synthesizing sugars with from three to seven carbon atoms in the chain. The pentose cycle is an important biosynthetic pathway in both plants and animals. In plants it represents the mechanism of synthesis of the carbon chain of sugars from carbon dioxide in photosynthesis. In animals its main function is probably the synthesis of the pentose sugars, which are of vital importance as constituents of nucleotides and nucleic acids. It may also play a part in

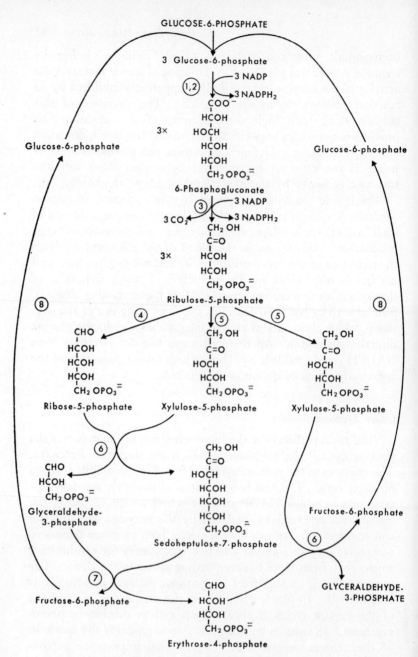

FIG. 12. The pentose cycle.

Enzymes: (1) glucose-6-phosphate dehydrogenase, (2) gluconolactonase,
(3) 6-phosphogluconate dehydrogenase, (4) phosphopentose isomerase,
(5) phosphoketopentose epimerase, (6) transketolase, (7) transaldolase,
(8) phosphohexoisomerase.

providing reducing equivalents in the form of $NADPH_2$ for use in various biosynthetic processes, such as the formation of fatty acids or proteins. Since the pentose cycle provides an alternate pathway, distinct from the Embden-Meyerhof sequence, for the degradation of glucose-6-phosphate to glyceraldehyde-3-phosphate, it could also operate as a mechanism for the catabolism of glucose in energy production. Investigation has shown, however, that in insects, as in other animals, the pentose cycle has little significance in energy production under normal conditions. Presumably the activity of the cycle is controlled by the ratio of $NADPH_2$ to NADP in the cytoplasm, and the presence in the cell of much more effective mechanisms for the reoxidation of $NADH_2$ than of $NADPH_2$ ensures that the main catabolic pathway is through the Embden-Meyerhof sequence. Under abnormal conditions, however, catabolism through the pentose cycle may be significant, since recent work has shown that a much higher than normal proportion of glucose is metabolized through the pentose cycle in insects poisoned with DDT. The probability that the pentose cycle plays a part in diapause metabolism has already been mentioned in Chapter i.

Oligosaccharides

Metabolism of trehalose

Trehalose, which is made up of two glucose units joined in a 1,1-α-linkage, is the characteristic blood sugar of insects, and in most species seems to have a physiological rôle comparable with that of glucose in the blood of vertebrates. Although the name trehalose commemorates a source of the sugar of insect derivation (the so-called 'trehala manna', which consists of dried cocoons of a Syrian beetle), trehalose was first isolated from ergot and was known chiefly as a metabolite of fungi and primitive plants, so that its rediscovery as a physiologically important sugar of insects was unexpected. Since then further search has established its presence in many invertebrate animals. Trehalose constitutes

Trehalose

the main labile energy source of many, probably most, insects,[77] its concentration being maintained in a state of dynamic equilibrium with the stored glycogen of the fat body. Degradation of trehalose is accomplished by the enzyme trehalase, which occurs along with its substrate in insect blood, and which hydrolyses the disaccharide to two molecules of glucose. Since the pathway from glycogen to trehalose involves the synthesis of uridine diphosphate glucose (UDPG) from glucose-1-phosphate, and results in the hydrolysis of one molecule of uridine triphosphate (UTP) to uridine diphosphate (UDP) for every molecule of trehalose formed (fig. 13), the use of trehalose rather than glucose as the labile energy source involves an extra energy-requiring step, and we might wonder what the selective advantage of such a system might be. One reason for preferring trehalose could be that the disaccharide, with the reducing groups of its constituent glucose moieties linked in a head to head configuration, is a relatively unreactive molecule, and thus can be stored in high concentrations in the haemolymph without the risk of promoting unwanted side reactions, such as could occur between reducing sugars and the amino acids which are also stored in high concentrations in the blood, but the fact that some insects do survive with a haemolymph loaded with reducing sugars suggests that this explanaton is inadequate.

It is interesting that the acceptor of the glucosyl group of UDPG in trehalose synthesis in insects, as in yeasts, is glucose-6-phosphate[41] (see fig. 13), whereas in the case of glycogen UDPG transglycosylase glucose units are added directly to the 4 position (or 6 position, in the case of the branching enzyme) of a growing glucosyl chain. The end product, in the first case, is a molecule of trehalose-6-phosphate, which is dephosphorylated by a specific enzyme found in insect tissues. Presumably the substitution of the 6 position in the acceptor molecule is necessary only for orientation on the enzyme to produce the 1,1 linkage of trehalose, since trehalose-6-phosphate is not known to undergo any metabolic conversions other than dephosphorylation. If, for instance, it could be split to glucose-6-phosphate and glucose, then the energetic disadvantage in the use of trehalose as a labile energy source would disappear.

Although phosphomonoesterases have been identified in insect tissues of all kinds, the specificity of these enzymes has received little attention. It is known that silkworm blood contains a specific glucose-1-phosphatase which is quite inactive against

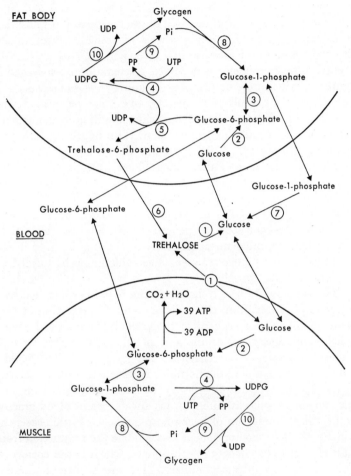

FIG. 13.   Metabolism of trehalose.

Enzymes: (1) trehalase, (2) hexokinase, (3) phosphoglucomutase, (4) UDPG pyrophosphorylase, (5) trehalose-6-phosphate UDPG transglycosylase, (6) trehalose-6-phosphatase, (7) glucose-1-phosphatase, (8) phosphorylase, (9) pyrophosphatase, (10) glycogen UDPG transglycosylase.

glucose-6-phosphate, and, in fact, the blood of this species contains an appreciable amount of glucose-6-phosphate. The route from glycogen to glucose is thus shorter by one step than it is in mammals, which possess a glucose-6-phosphatase. It is not known whether this condition is general for insects, but if so, it might be a consequence of the need to reserve glucose-6-phosphate as a starting point for the synthesis of trehalose-6-phosphate, although some physical separation of enzyme activities would be needed to make this effective. Such a separation is envisaged in figure 13, which may be useful as a summary of some aspects of carbohydrate metabolism in insects, but must be treated with caution, as it is based on knowledge which is still quite inadequate. Some of the metabolic events shown in figure 13 are well established, however. It is known that the fat body is the site of trehalose synthesis, and that when blood trehalose is depleted during muscular activity it is rapidly resynthesized at the expense of fat body glycogen or of blood glucose. Glycogen is also synthesized from UDPG in the fat body, as well as in muscle. Trehalose does not seem to penetrate with any ease into flight muscle, but is rapidly metabolized by intact muscle, presumably after hydrolysis to glucose by enzymes which may be located on the surface of the muscle.

The concentration of trehalose in the blood is controlled by a hormone produced from the corpora cardiaca. Injection of very small amounts of corpus cardiacum extract leads to a rise in blood trehalose but does not affect the concentration of reducing sugars.[67] The source of the extra trehalose is the glycogen of the fat body, and the effect of adding the hormone is stimulation of the activity of the fat body phosphorylase. In mammals, glucagon and catecholamines such as adrenalin produce a rise in blood glucose by a similar stimulation of liver phosphorylase. In this case, the primary effect of the hormone is to stimulate the production from ATP of cyclic adenosine-3′,5′-phosphate, which is the coenzyme of the active form of phosphorylase. The mechanism of stimulation may well be the same in insects, and the corpus cardiacum hormone may be one of the several catecholamines (including adrenalin) which have been extracted from insects. The enzyme responsible for the formation of the cyclic nucleotide has been identified in insects.

Other oligosaccharides

Oligosaccharides formed by insect enzymes have been isolated from honey, and from the honeydew of aphids and other plant bugs. They are formed as a result of the glycosyl-transferring activities of the digestive enzymes of the insects. Thus honeybee invertase not only hydrolyses sucrose to glucose and fructose, but also transfers glucosyl units to the glucose end of sucrose to produce gluco-sucrose and higher oligosaccharides of the same nature. The invertases of plant bugs also seem to be glucosyl-transferring enzymes, but whereas some produce gluco-sucrose others form melizitose, by transferring glucose to the 3 position of the fructosyl part of sucrose. Melizitose was first isolated from insect honeydew and is well known as a contaminant of the honey of bees feeding on honeydew.

Sucrose, the characteristic storage disaccharide of plants, is not regarded as a normal animal product, but has been reported in appreciable concentration in the blood of the silkworm. Although the identification is not above question, it is probable that further investigation will add sucrose to the long list of characteristic plant and fungal metabolites elaborated by the metabolically versatile insects.

Polysaccharides

Metabolism of chitin

Chitin, a polymer of N-acetylglucosamine units in 1,4-β-linkages, is regarded as the characteristic polysaccharide of the arthropods, although it is also found in other animals and in fungal cell walls. In insects, chitin is one of the main constituents of the exoskeleton, and is produced by most cells of ectodermal

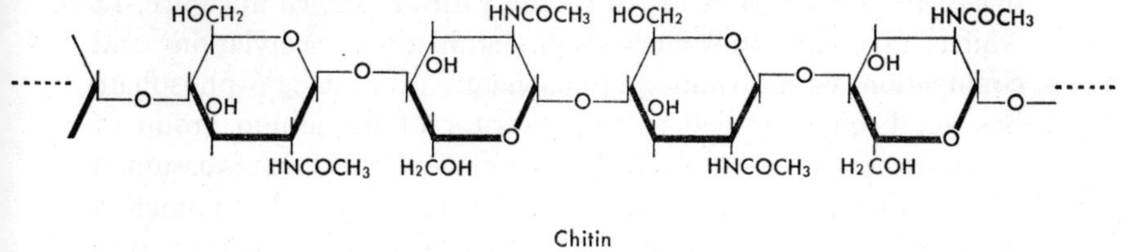

Chitin

origin, lining the fore and hind guts and also most tracheae. The peritrophic membrane, a tube which is produced from the end of the foregut and encloses the food during passage through the alimentary canal, also has a high chitin content.

Insects grow by a series of moults, rebuilding the entire exoskeleton from time to time, and reabsorbing much of the old cuticle before it is shed, so it is clear that carbohydrate metabolism associated with chitin synthesis must be very active. Glucose in the blood can be incorporated into newly forming cuticle, and carbohydrate derived from the old cuticle may be stored in the body in the form of sugar or glycogen, and may even be converted to a small extent into fat. There is, however, a considerable degree of specific reuse of the carbohydrate of the old cuticle in the formation of the new, since radioactively labelled glucose incorporated into the cuticle may reappear there after a second moult. The molecular species of the reused material has not been established. It does not appear in analyses for carbohydrate, and it has been suggested that it may be in the form of a glycoprotein. Chitin is formed from glucose in the wing epidermis of the young adult locust by the pathway shown in figure, 14 which involves phosphorylation, amination, acetylation and conjugation with uridine diphosphate.[11] Fructose-6-phosphate has not been identified as the acceptor of the amino group of glutamine in the synthesis of glucosamine in insects, but is assumed to play this part by analogy with the bacterial and mammalian systems for the synthesis of glucosamine. Similarly, the

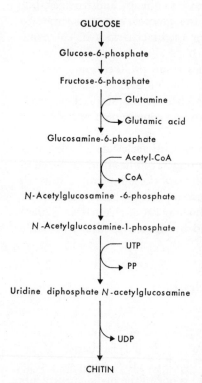

FIG. 14. Pathway of chitin synthesis.

conversion of N-acetylglucosamine-6-phosphate to N-acetylglucosamine-1-phosphate has not been demonstrated but is believed to be a necessary preliminary to the formation of uridine diphosphate N-acetylglucosamine (UDPNAG), since in this compound, as in other conjugates of sugars with UDP, the nucleotide is linked to the 1 position of the carbohydrate. A low rate of synthesis of a chitin-like polymer from UDPNAG has been demonstrated in homogenates of whole insects. The mechanism of chitin synthesis is thus apparently analogous to that of the synthesis of glycogen and other glycosides.

Insect cuticle contains large amounts of protein as well as chitin. Most cuticles have about equal amounts of protein and chitin, but in some the chitin content may be very low, and others, such as that lining the smaller tracheal branches, have no chitin at all. It seems that much of the chitin in the cuticle may be joined to the protein by covalent bonds, which suggests that the basic material of insect cuticle may be glycoprotein. ' Chitin ', as used for biological and chemical studies is derived from natural material, and although soft untanned cuticle is used and is treated to remove protein, there is some uncertainty as to just what bonds are split in this ' purification '. This fact has contributed to the uncertainty regarding the chemical composition of insect chitin. Although all samples on hydrolysis reveal a preponderance of N-acetylglucosamine units, there is always a small and variable percentage of glucosamine and also some free amino groups. The latter are mostly aspartyl and histidyl residues, and probably represent some of the points of protein linkage.[28] The mode of attachment of such amino acid residues to the glycosyl chain is not known, but if the chitin polymer as formed contained a number of glucosamine units, then it would seem that these would be appropriate points for the attachment of polypeptide chains, either before or after deposition of the two components in the cuticle. Some of the protein of the cuticle is present in a free state, however, since it may be extracted from soft cuticles by such mild procedures as suggest that it is held only by hydrogen bonds, and it is likely that some chitin also occurs in a free state. Some cuticles are laminated, with alternate layers of chitin and protein. Although such laminations could arise by ' crystallization ' of preformed glycoproteins during dehydration of the new cuticle, their existence does suggest that chitin and protein are secreted sequentially, and that cross bonding occurs after deposition. Cross bonding of the protein fraction by specific agents after or during deposition is believed to be responsible for the production of the hardened pigmented protein ' sclerotin ' and of the rubber-like protein ' resilin ' (see Chapters 6 and 8), and a similar mechanism could account for chitin-protein interaction. On the other hand, the suggestion noted above that cuticular carbohydrate is stored preparatory to reuse as glycoprotein could imply that specific chitin-protein conjugates are synthesized by the dermal cells and are deposited as such in cuticle formation. There is still much to be learned about the synthesis and deposition of the cuticular components.

At the beginning of the moulting process a small amount of fluid, called the exuvial fluid, is secreted between the partly formed new cuticle and the old skeleton. This fluid contains enzymes which degrade the softer parts of the old cuticle to units small enough to be absorbed through the underlying new cuticle. Included among these enzymes are a chitinase and probably a chitobiase, capable between them of converting chitin to N-acetylglucosamine. Chitinase splits chitin to oligosaccharides, the smallest of which would be the disaccharide chitobiose. Further degradation is then the function of a second enzyme, which may be called chitobiase, which produces N-acetylglucosamine from the biose and higher oligosaccharides. Exuvial fluid is difficult to obtain, and its enzyme content remains uncertain, but insects have been found to contain one or more chitinases, as well as other enzymes splitting the β-linkages of N-acetylglucosamine polymers. These are found in several tissues, particularly in the gut, where they may have a digestive function, but they are also prominent in the blood.[55] The chitinase activity, which may be due to more than one enzyme, is separable from the chitobiase activity, which may also be multiple, and both are distinct from the β-glucosidases, which, as mentioned earlier, also have a wide distribution in insect tissues.

Other polysaccharides

Glycogen is the main storage polysaccharide of insects, as of other animals, and is stored in many cells, especially those of the fat body and muscle. The chemistry of insect glycogen has not been studied; it is assumed to be identical with the long branched chain of glucose units found in mammals, with 1,4 linkages along the chain and 1,6 linkages at the branches. Insects degrade glycogen and starch to maltose with digestive amylases, which, although not studied in detail, are probably similar in action to mammalian enzymes.

Most animals synthesize a number of glycoproteins, or mucins, as they are also called, which perform a variety of structural and lubricating functions. Knowledge of the chemistry of these substances is still scanty, but the polysaccharide components are known to be rich in aminated and sulphated sugars, usually joined in β linkages. They contain, for instance, glucosamine and galactosamine and their N-acetyl derivatives, as well as glucuronic and galacturonic acids and chondroitin sulphate. Apart from chitin itself, mucopolysaccharides of these kinds were not known as insect products until quite recently, but it now seems certain that insects do elaborate a number of mucopolysaccharides. A polysaccharide containing N-acetylgalactosamine has been reported from insect blood, which also contains the UDP derivative of this sugar. The peritrophic membrane of the silkworm, which performs the same function as does the mucous secretion of the alimentary canal of mammals, contains in addition to chitin and protein a polysaccharide made up of equimolar amounts of glucuronic acid and N-acetylglucosamine, which has been identified as hyaluronic acid.[51] Hyaluronic acid may have other minor functions in insects, but its importance in animals protected by an exoskeleton is clearly much less than in mammals, where it serves as a cementing substance in the subcutaneous tissues.

The β-glucosidases of insect tissues probably play a part in the degradation of mucopolysaccharides. Insects also produce the enzyme hyaluronidase in special glands. Thus the presence of this enzyme in wasp venom probably promotes the penetration of the toxic principle in vertebrate tissues, while the hyaluronidase in the saliva of carnivorous bugs may assist in the liquefaction of the tissues of their victims. A comparable enzyme, pectinase, found in the salivary secretion of aphids, aids the penetration of the insect's stylets by hydrolysing the α linkages of the galacturonic acid polymer, pectin.

4 : Lipid Metabolism

Storage Fats

Much of the food eaten by insects during larval life is converted into fat, and stored in the cells of the fat body. Some of this fat disappears during the pupal period, being degraded to provide the energy and perhaps the starting material for some of the bio-synthetic processes associated with metamorphosis, but much may persist into adult life. It continues to serve as an energy reserve in the adult, although in female insects most is converted into the protein and lipid of the developing eggs. Metabolism directed towards fat synthesis is retained in some adult insects. Thus butterflies and moths continue to synthesize fat when fed only on sugar, as does also the female mosquito, but male mosquitoes do not convert carbohydrate into fat, nor do male or female houseflies. Clearly fat metabolism is of great importance in the economy of insects, and the main trend of such metabolism—towards synthesis, or oxidation, or interconversion—may change during the life cycle.

Depot fats of animals are usually in the form of triglycerides, that is, esters formed by the combination of glycerol with three fatty acids, each of which comprises a long straight hydrocarbon chain of usually 14 to 20 carbon atoms. Several reports in the older literature have indicated that some depot fats of insects may contain an unusually high proportion of free fatty acids, but recent work has failed to reveal any such instances, and the validity of the older findings may be questionable.[23] The fatty acid composition of insect storage fat varies considerably from species to species. The composition varies to some extent with diet in some insects, but in others is quite independent of differences in diet.   An effect of the fatty acid composition of the diet on the kinds of fatty acids deposited in the fat body is seen especially in insects on a high fat diet, such as those living in oily seeds.   In most animal fats the predominant acids are the sixteen- and eighteen-carbon saturated members, palmitic and stearic, and the eighteen-carbon unsaturated oleic acid, with one double bond; the majority of plant fats and oils are less saturated, and include acids with several double bonds.   Included within the insects are many species in which the fatty acid composition is similar to that of the majority of animals, but the full range of variation is very wide—from fats containing almost exclusively saturated fatty acids to those in which the degree of unsaturation is as high as in any vegetable oil. Some fats of quite unusual composition have been found in members of the Aphididae.   According to an early report, the fat of a gall-forming species of *Pemphigus* would seem to be made up almost entirely of saturated fatty acids of very short chain length. More recent work has established that the composition of the fat of this and other genera, although unusual, is less startling than at first thought.   Aphid fats in general have a very high proportion of the saturated fourteen-carbon myristic acid, appreciable amounts of a nine-carbon acid, and much smaller, but measurable, quantities of the acids of shorter chain length, down to the four-carbon butyric acid.

Metabolism of Fatty Acids and Glycerides

Synthesis of fatty acids

Fatty acids are synthesized from two carbon units derived ultimately from acetate.   The thioester of malonic acid and coenzyme A (malonyl-CoA) is a key intermediate in the synthetic mechanism.   The initial reaction is believed to be the condensation of acetyl-CoA with malonyl-CoA with the liberation of carbon dioxide and the formation of a four-carbon keto compound, which can then condense with a second molecule of malonyl-CoA:

$$CH_3.CO\text{-}SCoA + \overset{\displaystyle COOH}{\underset{}{CH_2}}.CO\text{-}SCoA \longrightarrow CH_3.CO.CH_2.CO\text{-}SCoA + CO_2 + CoA$$

acetyl-CoA   malonyl-CoA   postulated four-carbon intermediate

This process is repeated until the complete carbon chain of the fatty acid is formed. Keto ($>C = O$) groups are reduced to methylenes ($>CH_2$) in a process in which $NADPH_2$ is the electron donor and which probably involves the intermediate formation of hydroxy ($>CHOH$) and alkene ($-CH = CH-$) derivatives. In a system which synthesizes a single fatty acid, only acetyl-CoA and malonyl-CoA seem to act as substrates; fatty acyl coenzyme A derivatives of intermediate chain length do not condense with malonyl-CoA, and none of the postulated intermediates in the pathway has been isolated. This suggests that the growing carbon chain may remain tightly bound to the enzyme while successive condensations take place and that there may be specific synthesizing enzymes for each fatty acid. Malonyl-CoA may be formed by carboxylation of acetyl-CoA in a reaction which involves the vitamin biotin. This accounts for the incorporation of acetate into the whole carbon skeleton of fatty acids, although only the first two carbon atoms (those most remote from the carboxyl group) are derived directly from acetyl-CoA. Only the bare outlines of the mechanism of fatty acid synthesis are known for any animal, and information on insects is similarly sketchy. *In vitro* fatty acid synthesis by insect fat body has been shown to depend on the addition of malonate, and it has been found that the pattern of incorporation of the carbon atoms of acetate into insect fatty acids is consistent with the pathway suggested above.

Although animals in general are capable of forming fatty acids with a single double bond, such as oleic acid, they have only a limited ability to synthesize acids with two or more double bonds, and may require a dietary source of such compounds. Several insects have also been found to need polyunsaturated fatty acids in the diet. Such requirements can usually be met by the ingestion of either linoleic acid (two double bonds) or linolenic acid (three double bonds). It is uncertain just how widespread this metabolic deficiency is; many insects seem to be capable of synthesizing their complete fatty acid requirements, and the storage of considerable amounts of polyunsaturated fatty acids by some insects suggests that there are no problems associated with their synthesis, but it is not clear to what extent micro-organisms are responsible for this synthetic ability. A pathway for the dehydrogenation of fatty acids to yield unsaturated derivatives has been found in some animal tissues, but has not been demonstrated in insects.

Synthesis of glycerides

In the formation of glycerides, fatty acyl coenzyme A derivatives condense with α-glycerophosphate to form first a phosphatidic acid, and then, by substitution of the phosphate group, a triglyceride. This pathway is also relatively unexplored in insects, although in vitro triglyceride synthesis from added acetate by cell free extracts has been established.

Hydrolysis of glycerides

Lipases, which are capable of hydrolysing the ester linkages binding fatty acids to glycerol, are known to occur in several tissues of insects. They may be quite active in muscle, particularly in those species which burn fat in flight, and are also found in the fat body. Since flight muscle mitochondria have been shown to be capable of oxidizing fatty acids to carbon dioxide and water, it seems that the flight muscles of insects such as the migratory locust can undertake the complete catabolism of lipids reaching them in the form of glycerides. Insects also secrete digestive lipases, which hydrolyse fats in their food. Apparently the fatty acids produced by the enzymes' action are effective in emulsifying that part of the fat which is absorbed unchanged, and thus aid its absorption, since special emulsifying agents, like the bile salts of mammals, are not produced.

Transport of fats

Fats absorbed by the gut are released into the blood, probably in the form of free fatty acids and glycerides. The fat body of the migratory locust has been shown to be capable of absorbing free fatty acids from the blood and converting them into glycerides. Conversely, the fat body releases glycerides into the blood in a process which is specific and stoichimetric for the amount of blood present.[68] The released glycerides are largely in the form of lipoprotein, and presumably this compound of glyceride and protein is the major molecular species engaged in the transport of fat from the fat body to the muscles when the latter are consuming fat in flight. It seems likely that some modification of the triglyceride structure would precede combination with protein, and the recent discovery of diglycerides combined with protein in insect blood suggests that the initial reaction is the removal of a fatty acyl residue.

Conversion of fat to carbohydrate

The existence of a common intermediate, acetyl-CoA, in the pathways for the catabolism of fats and carbohydrates suggests

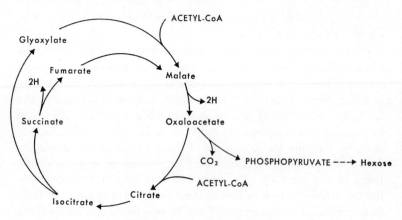

FIG. 15.   The glyoxylate cycle.

that no difficulty should be encountered in the conversion of the former into the latter. This conversion is not. characteristic of animal metabolism, however, and in those organisms in which it does occur, it is effected by a special route, known as the glyoxylate cycle. The cycle, which is illustrated in figure 15, is initiated by the condensation of acetyl-CoA with glyoxylate to form malate, a reaction catalysed by the enzyme malate synthetase. Malate is converted to isocitrate by the enzymes of the citric acid cycle, then isocitrate is cleaved by the enzyme isocitric lyase to yield succinate and glyoxylate. Succinate is converted to malate by citric acid cycle enzymes to complete the cycle. Oxaloacetate is believed to be the main source of carbohydrate formed during the operation of the glyoxylate cycle, probably by conversion to phosphopyruvate, followed by reversal of the Embden-Meyerhof pathway to yield hexose. One revolution of the cycle thus converts two molecules of acetyl-CoA to one molecule of phosphopyruvate and one molecule of carbon dioxide, and yields four atoms of hydrogen for energy production. The glyoxylate cycle is found in some bacteria and in germinating oily seeds, where the conversion of fat to sugar is an important metabolic requirement. A condition similar to that of a germinating seed might be thought to exist during pupation in insects, when fat stored up during larval life is used as a source of the carbon chains of many body constituents. A search for the glyoxylate cycle has therefore been made, in spite of the fact that it is not known to occur in any other animal. The key enzymes, malate synthetase and isocitric lyase, have been identified in the pupa of one insect (the southern army worm), but the activities reported in a preliminary communication are low: it is therefore still not known whether the glyoxylate cycle has any real importance in insect metabolism.

Compound Lipids

Fatty acid glycerides appear to have no metabolic function; they exist solely as energy and carbon stores. The metabolically active fats, which are built into the structure of all cells, are the so-called compound lipids. These are combinations of fatty acids with a variety of residues, including glycerol, nitrogenous bases, carbohydrates, amino acids, phosphate and sulphate. The importance of the compound lipids in the architecture and metabolism of the cell has become increasingly obvious as the science of biochemistry has developed, but effective methods for the study of their chemistry and metabolism are only now being developed, so that even their chemistry is uncertain and information on their rôle in biology is meagre.

The commonest and best known compound lipids are the phosphatide derivatives, in which the basic molecular skeleton is that of α-glycerophosphate with the phosphate group engaged in a second ester linkage with either choline, ethanolamine, serine or inositol. Such phosphatides in which the remaining two alcoholic groups of the glyceryl residue are combined in ester linkage with fatty acids are known as phosphatidylcholines (lecithins), phosphatidylethanolamines, etc. (fig. 16). Phosphatides of these four types occur in insects, but in relative quantities which may differ greatly from the distribution found in mammals.[23] Lecithins are

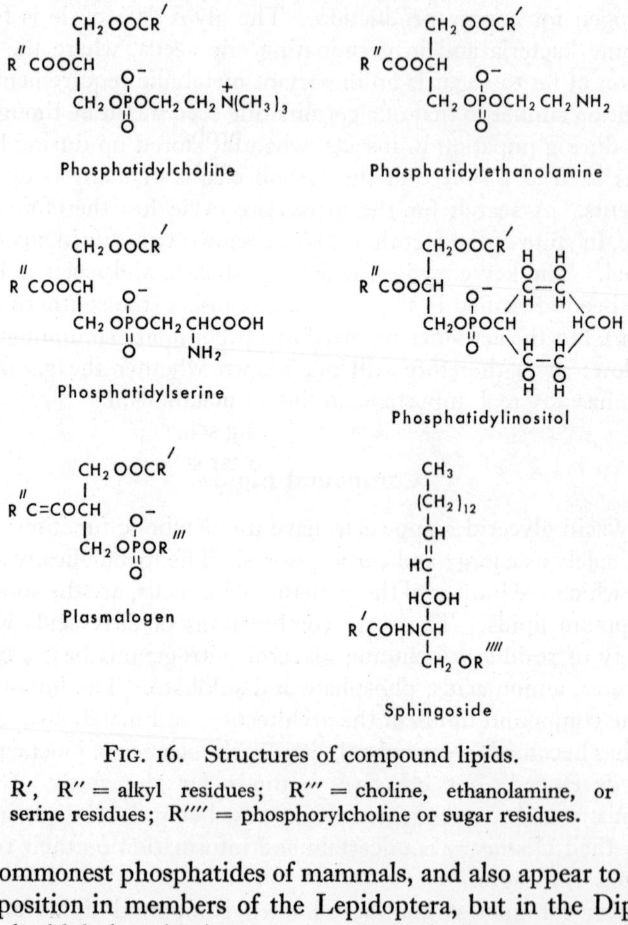

FIG. 16.   Structures of compound lipids.

R′, R″ = alkyl residues; R‴ = choline, ethanolamine, or serine residues; R‴‴ = phosphorylcholine or sugar residues.

the commonest phosphatides of mammals, and also appear to hold this position in members of the Lepidoptera, but in the Diptera phosphatidylethanolamines are quantitatively the most important. A study of the incorporation of labelled phosphate into the phosphatides of a moth, *Arctia caja*, has suggested that the phosphatidylinositols are metabolically the most active lipids in this insect.

Unlike most animals, insects are unable to synthesize their full requirements of choline, and must rely on their diet to supply most of their needs of this phospholipid component. It has been established that carnitine can replace choline in the diets of some insects, and it has been found that when these species are fed on a diet supplemented with carnitine they contain a new phosphatide in which the nitrogenous base is methylcholine instead of choline. Inositol is also an essential nutrient for some insects. There is some evidence that the insecticide benzene hexachloride, the molecule of which is structurally similar to that of inositol, may interfere with the metabolism of inositol lipids in insects. Inositol does not relieve the symptoms of acute benzene hexachloride poisoning, but does counteract the effects of feeding sublethal doses of the insecticide. One of these effects is the accumulation of unusually large amounts of cholesterol in the tissues of poisoned insects, so it is conceivable that the site of action of the insecticide might be the lipoprotein-sterol complexes of the cell's structure.

In phosphatides of a second type, known as plasmalogens, one of the alkyl chains yields on hydrolysis from the glyceryl residue an aldehyde, rather than an acid. The plasmalogens thus have one fatty acid residue in an ester linkage and one fatty aldehyde in an un-saturated ether linkage (fig. 16). Plasmalogens containing choline, ethanolamine and inositol have been identified in insect lipids, but seem to be quantitatively less important than in mammals.

In a group of compound lipids which may be classified as sphingosides the glycerol skeleton is replaced by the nitrogenous base sphingosine (fig. 16). The fatty acid is attached to the amino group of this compound through a peptide (NH-CO) linkage, while the alcoholic group may form an ester linkage with phos-phorylcholine (as in sphingomyelin), or a glycosidic linkage with a sugar (as in the cerebrosides). These lipids are particularly abundant in nervous tissue, as are also the more complex ganglio-sides, which are sphingosides containing fatty acyl, sugar and amino sugar residues. Sphingosides have been identified in insects, although reliable analyses of the compound lipids of two members of the Diptera have failed to reveal sphingomyelin. The housefly, which has no sphingomyelin, nor lipids incorporating sugars, contains a sphingolipid of possibly new structure incorporating an ethanolamine residue.

M.I.—G

Although sulphate is a prominent constituent of the compound lipids extracted from animals, very little is known about the structure or metabolism of the sulpholipids. Apart from a report that the lipids of some insects contain sulphur, nothing is known about this class of metabolite in insects.

The synthesis of lecithin involves the formation of phosphoryl-choline by phosphate transfer from ATP, then condensation with cytidine triphosphate to form cytidine diphosphate choline, in a reaction analogous to the formation of UDPG. Cytidine diphosphate choline then transfers the choline residue to a di-alkyl phosphatidic acid to form phosphatidylcholine. Analogous pathways accomplish the biosynthesis of other phospholipids. Neither the mechanisms nor the sites of synthesis of compound lipids have been studied in insects.

Degradation of the compound lipids is achieved by the action of a number of specific esterases. Phosphatases capable of hydrolysing the phosphate ester linkages of phospholipids are of wide occurrence in insect tissues, and presumably further degradation of the diglycerides formed by their action can be achieved by lipases. The venoms of bees and wasps and the saliva of a predaceous bug are known to contain lecithinases which are similar in action to, although much weaker than, the phospholipases of snake venom. These enzymes split one fatty acid from lecithin to yield lysolecithin, which is a powerful haemolytic agent in mammals, and is responsible for part of the toxicity of the venoms.

Waxes

Nearly all insects have an external coating of wax, resembling in its chemistry and its waterproofing function the cuticular wax of plants. Some insects secrete wax in large quantities, using it either as a protective covering, as in several coccids, or as material for nest building, as in the honeybee. Such waxes have been gathered by man since prehistoric times and used for his own purposes. Much of our knowledge of the chemical composition of insect waxes is based on analyses of waxes collected and processed for commerce, which may have suffered chemical changes between the time of secretion by the insect and eventual analysis. Moreover, until quite recent times the available chemical methods did not permit close discrimination between members of an homologous series of hydrocarbon derivatives, so for this reason, also, much of the older literature is of only limited value as a guide to the composition of the cuticular secretions of insects. There have been some analyses of fresh insect waxes by more modern techniques, however, and these have established our knowledge of the chemistry of the waxes on firmer ground. Most animal waxes are sterol esters, but insect waxes contain either no sterol, or only minor amounts, the main alcohol component being, in fact, the straight-chain, *n*-series primary alcohols. All insect waxes are mixtures, often of numerous constituents.[23, 24] Free *n*-series paraffins always seem to be a major component, but esters of fatty acids and primary alcohols, as well as acids and alcohols in the free state, are also found. Chain lengths of the paraffins and fatty acids vary from about 12 to 34 carbon atoms, while primary alcohols of from 20 to 36 carbon atoms have been identified. Both saturated and unsaturated hydrocarbon derivatives have been recognized, along with a proportion of hydroxy derivatives in beeswax, keto derivatives in some coccid waxes, and aldehydes in the cuticular wax of the American cockroach. In general, the fatty acids and alcohols have even-numbered and the paraffins odd-numbered carbon chains, but this rule is not invariable. The melting points of natural insect waxes cover a fairly wide range, the variation being due, in part, to differences in chain length of the components, but, more importantly, to the presence in lower melting point waxes of fatty acids and paraffins with one or more double bonds. Some insect waxes are known to harden on exposure to air, and, indeed, a change from a mobile liquid to a hard wax may be a general phenomenon accompanying wax secretion. It has been suggested that this change is the result of the evaporation of volatile constituents, but analyses have so far failed to confirm this. It seems more probable that hardening is the result of the oxidation of unsaturated components along with the cross reactions and polymerizations in which the reactive alkyl aldehyde components might be expected to engage.

In many insects the wax includes a harder component known as the cement layer, which may well be the result of the secretion at a special time of a higher proportion of reactive lipids which polymerize to form resins. Sometimes the cement layer is on the surface of the wax, but in other species a waxy bloom is present outside the cement layer. Polymers, in the form of acidic resins of varying molecular weight, have been identified as a major component (12–14 per cent.) of the cuticular wax of a cricket, *Anabrus simplex*. Resinous compounds are important constituents of shellac, which is extracted from the waxy tests of a coccid. The secretion of chemically active lipids may also play a part in the formation of the outer layers of the cuticle itself. The non-chitinous epicuticle, which constitutes a layer 1–2 μ thick covering the much thicker chitinous endocuticle, seems to contain several components, and may differ in chemistry from species to species, but has as a major constituent the substance known as ' cuticulin ', which is resistant to lipid solvents and cold mineral acids, and seems to be of a lipoprotein nature. It may be secreted as such, or could be formed by cross reactions between reactive lipids and proteins secreted separately. After an old cuticle is shed, the newly formed epicuticle is still more strongly cross linked by quinones, in the hardening and darkening process which also affects the outer layers of the endocuticle (see Chapter 6). Quinone-induced cross bonding and polymerization may also affect some of the purely lipid components of the cuticle, since an outer layer of some cuticles, which is even more resistant to chemical attack than the cuticulin layer, seems to contain no protein, and may be a completely polymerized resin, although its chemical nature is still undecided. Both the cuticulin of the epicuticle and the cross-linked lipid layer external to it, are distinct from the outer waxy covering, which, even when it contains some resinous material, may readily be removed by lipid solvents.

Studies on the physical properties of the cuticular wax and their relations to water permeability have suggested that the innermost layer of the wax is probably in the form of an oriented monolayer, perhaps formed by the attraction of polar groups to the hydrated layers of the cuticle. Rising temperature is said to cause a sudden increase in permeability by disrupting the mono-layer at a transition temperature which is characteristic for the insect species. Transition temperatures of different species can be correlated to some extent with the conditions of their environments, being highest, for instance, in those insects living in hot, dry situations. Although the postulated monolayer may be an important factor in the control of permeability, it is not the only one, since the amount, nature and physical architecture of the wax layer are also involved. Very few insect cuticles lack a water-proofing layer of some sort. The only completely permeable cuticles may be those of organs physiologically concerned with water absorption or in which water absorption is an unavoidable corollary of oxygen absorption, as in the gills of some aquatic larvae.

We have no knowledge of the mechanisms of synthesis of any but the fatty acid components of insect wax. Since the derivation of fatty acids by condensation of two-carbon units results in a preponderance of acids with even-numbered chains, a mechanism of paraffin synthesis by decarboxylation of fatty acids would explain the preponderance of paraffins with odd-numbered chains. It is also apparent that a pathway that by-passed some of the reductive steps in the series of reactions leading to the formation of saturated fatty acids could produce acids with keto or hydroxyl groups, or with double bonds, but whether such compounds are synthesized by such a mechanism, or by secondary reactions imposed on saturated derivatives, is entirely a matter of speculation.

Larvae of the wax moth, which live in bee hives, have an unusual ability to digest the beeswax which forms a large part of their diet. They can absorb and metabolize to some extent all the components of the wax. It is probable that bacteria present in the gut of the moth are responsible for the degradation of the wax to absorbable components. Absorption and metabolism of derivatives of the wax seems to be accompanied by an unusually active phosphorus metabolism, since the excreta of the moth contain a high concentration of phosphorus in the form of pyrophosphate and other more highly polymerized polyphosphates. This phenomenon has already been discussed in Chapter 2.

Hydrocarbon Derivatives with Special Functions in Physiology

Much of the instinctive behaviour of insects is released by the stimulation of the chemical senses of smell and taste, and insects themselves produce many chemical compounds which affect the behaviour of other individuals. Such substances are particularly important in the social insects, where much cooperative behaviour is elicited by odour stimuli, and where metabolites transferred from one individual to another may directly affect physiology and even morphology by control of the direction of development. Such substances, produced by one individual and influencing the behaviour or physiology of other individuals of a species, have been called pheromones, by analogy with the hormones which carry out similar functions within the body of an individual. Pheromones have been the subject of intense study over the last few years, and several have been isolated and chemically identified.[38] They have mostly turned out to be alkyl aldehydes, ketones, alcohols, acids, or esters, related chemically to the aliphatic compounds of the cuticular waxes. Moreover, they are probably all produced by ectodermal glands of one kind or another, although these may be located on almost any part of the body, from the mandibular glands of the head to the anal or pygidial glands of the last abdominal segment. In other insects, the secretions of the dermal glands may constitute a chemical defence mechanism. They may act by endowing the insect with an odour or taste that is repugnant to birds or other predators, or they may be toxic mixtures, often propelled with force and aimed with intent, which are capable of repelling or even killing attackers, especially when these are other arthropods. In some species, particularly in ants, the pheromone and defensive functions may be combined, the odour trail which one species follows often being repugnant to other insects.

Pheromones

The ability of virgin female moths to attract males from seemingly incredible distances has for many years excited the admiration and interest of biologists. That the males are attracted through the sense of smell was established long before any of the chemical attractants were isolated. The scent glands of moths secrete into a pair of evertible sacs well supplied with hairs, which are situated at the end of the abdomen. Production of the sex attractant ceases soon after copulation. The active principles are produced in quite small amounts, so that the task of collecting sufficient material for chemical isolation is not easy, and any successful identification may well be regarded as a triumph of analytical chemistry. The first sex attractant to be identified, which was that of the silk moth, *Bombyx mori*, was found to be an unsaturated straight-chain alcohol, hexadeca-(10,12)-dienol:

$$CH_3.(CH_2)_2.\underset{\underset{H}{|}}{C}=\underset{\underset{H}{|}}{C}.\overset{\overset{H}{|}}{C}=\underset{\underset{H}{|}}{C}.(CH_2)_8.CH_2OH.$$

The sex attractant of the gypsy moth, *Porthetria dispar*, is a similar unsaturated alcohol, but in this case with a secondary alcoholic group engaged in ester linkage with acetic acid—*cis*-10-acetoxy hexadec-7-enol:

$$CH_3.(CH_2)_5.\underset{\underset{O=\overset{|}{C}.CH_3}{\underset{|}{O}}}{CH}.CH_2.\underset{\underset{H}{|}}{C}=\underset{\underset{H}{|}}{C}.(CH_2)_5.CH_2OH.$$

An ester of shorter chain length (*trans*-2-hexenyl acetate) had earlier been extracted from an aquatic bug, *Lethocerus indicus*. This compound, which has a cinnamon-like smell, is produced from dorsal abdominal glands in the male only, and for this reason has been considered to be a sex attractant. Its function has not been established by physiological studies, however, and so remains undecided. The bugs are of interest in that they are used for flavouring food in Asia, adding a spicy taste that is traceable to the presence of the ester. Even the American cockroach, unattractive as it is to human senses, wafts an exciting aroma to the antennae of its mate, the active principle of which has been reported to be the ester of a complex alcohol with a three-membered ring structure. This identification has been challenged, however, so a final answer on the cockroach sex attractant must await the outcome of further work. The sex attractants can excite members of the opposite sex at fantastically low dilution—so low that it seems that the collision of only a few molecules with the sense organs must be sufficient to trigger the response. They are generally species-specific, and the response is highly specific in a chemical sense; analogues which differ only minutely from the structure of the true attractant (such as by a change in configuration about a double bond) may have very much reduced potency.

Probably all social insects communicate by chemical means to some extent. Ants, in particular, follow odour trails to and from the nest, and honeybees use a chemical marker to identify a source of nectar, supplementing this with the informational dance at the entrance to the hive. The formic acid secreted by the anal glands of formicine ants may act to some extent as a trail marker, as well as being the main component of the defensive and offensive armament. The dolichoderine ants produce several strong-smelling ketones, as well as more complex cyclic compounds of the terpene variety, from their anal glands. These secretions probably have several functions, but the more volatile short-chain members, at least, are probably important in trail marking. They include 2-methylhept-2-en-6-one

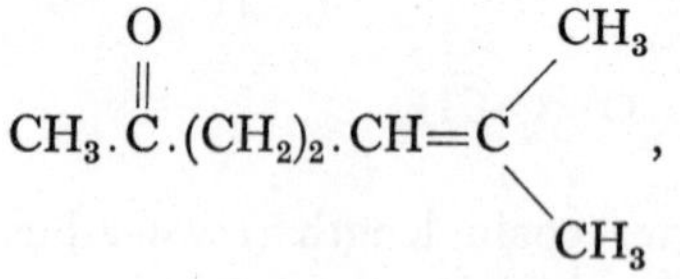

$$CH_3 . \overset{\overset{O}{\|}}{C} . (CH_2)_2 . CH{=}C \overset{\displaystyle CH_3}{\underset{\displaystyle CH_3}{\big<}} \quad ,$$

2-methylheptan-4-one

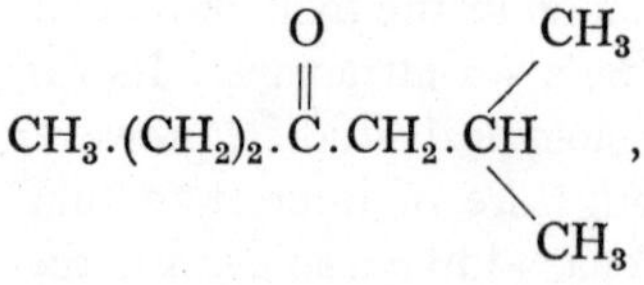

$$CH_3 . (CH_2)_2 . \overset{\overset{O}{\|}}{C} . CH_2 . CH \overset{\displaystyle CH_3}{\underset{\displaystyle CH_3}{\big<}} \quad ,$$

4-methylhexan-2-one

$$CH_3 . CH_2 . \overset{\overset{\displaystyle CH_3}{|}}{CH} . CH_2 . \overset{\overset{O}{\|}}{C} . CH_3,$$

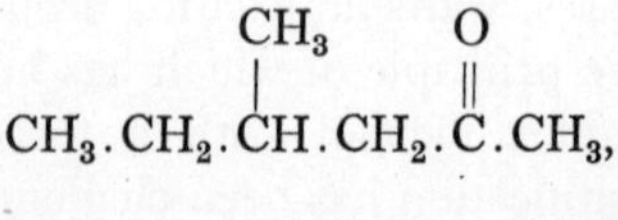

and the saturated ketone tridecan-12-one. Since the composition of the anal gland secretions may vary between different colonies of the one species of ant, the trail odour may be to some extent specific for a single nest. The marking substance of the worker honeybee is produced from the Nassonoff organ, a gland situated on the seventh abdominal tergite, which is everted at an abundant source of nectar and serves to attract other bees to the site. The odour is also emitted at the entrance to the hive, and, along with perhaps more specific hive odours, aids the homing of workers. The active principle is the terpene alcohol geraniol (fig. 17). The unsaturated alcohol *cis*-hex-3-enol is probably a trail marker for

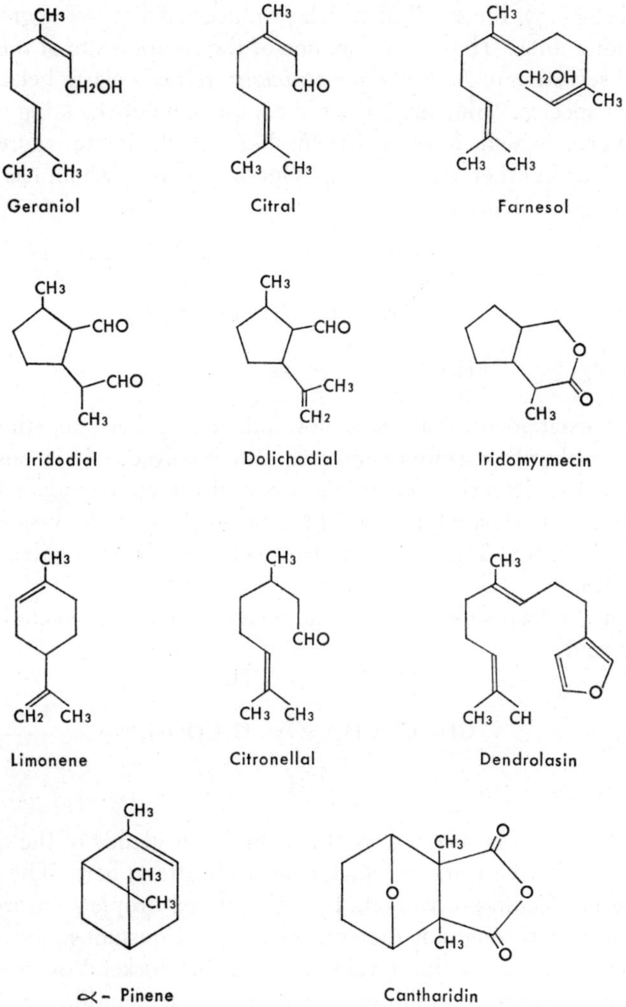

Geraniol

Citral

Farnesol

Iridodial

Dolichodial

Iridomyrmecin

Limonene

Citronellal

Dendrolasin

α - Pinene

Cantharidin

FIG. 17.   Insect terpenoids.

the termite, *Calotermes flavicollis*, since it can be extracted from the termites and also their galleries, and its odour is attractive to them. Substances which elicit the alarm reaction, summoning members of the soldier class and arousing aggressive behaviour, are important in the biology of social insects. The leaf-cutting ant, *Atta sexdens*, secretes from mandibular glands the aldehyde citral (fig. 17), the smell of which produces a frenzy of aggression in soldier ants. Heptan-2-one, one of the components of the anal gland secretion of *Iridomyrmex pruinosus*, releases alarm behaviour in this species. Similarly, volatile components of the sting of the honeybee, which have a banana-like smell, incite aggressive behaviour in other worker bees. One compound, which has been isolated and identified as *iso*-amylacetate,

$$\begin{array}{c} H_3C \\ \diagdown \\ CH.CH_2.CH_2O{-}\overset{\displaystyle O}{\overset{\displaystyle \|}{C}}.CH_3, \\ \diagup \\ H_3C \end{array}$$

causes excitement, but does not induce the bees to sting, so presumably other components are also involved. It is possible that all the defensive secretions of social insects contain volatile alarm substances, and more physiological work is needed to determine the functions of the compounds recognized by chemists.

The ' queen substance ' of the honeybee is *trans*-9-ketodec-2-enoic acid:

$$CH_3.\overset{\displaystyle O}{\overset{\displaystyle \|}{C}}.(CH_2)_5.\overset{\displaystyle H}{\overset{\displaystyle |}{C}}=\overset{\displaystyle |}{\underset{\displaystyle H}{C}}.COOH.$$

This fatty acid is secreted by the mandibular glands of the queen and eaten by the workers which constantly attend her. The habit of mutual feeding of workers by regurgitated droplets ensures its distribution throughout the entire colony. Constant ingestion of the acid suppresses the development of the workers' ovaries and prevents them from building queen cells. The mandibular glands of the queen also produce a substance, as yet unidentified, which attracts workers. A third pheromone, which may be produced generally over the body surface, is said to reinforce the action of the ketodecenoic acid. As might be expected of a compound which produces such a profound metabolic effect as the queen substance, the action is not species-specific. Repeated injections of ketodecenoic acid also inhibit ovary development in the house-fly. The mandibular glands of the worker bees secrete a fatty acid, 10-hydroxy-dec-2-enoic acid, which is closely related to the queen substance, but is not known to have any pheromone activity. It is added to the larval food placed in brood cells, being in particularly high concentration in the ' royal jelly ' which nourishes the future queen. It seems not to be responsible for the greater ovarian development of the queen, however, and may act primarily as an antibiotic preservative of the food.

In other social insects pheromones of even more startling metabolic effect are apparently transferred from individual to individual. Thus, in the termites, the supernumerary moults undergone by the ' pseudoergate ' workers may result in the production of either winged reproductives or the morphologically dissimilar soldiers. The direction in which development proceeds is influenced by the presence or absence of soldiers in the colony. This suggests that a pheromone is circulated which is capable of releasing the expression of one whole set of genes, while suppressing another set. The nature of this pheromone is not known, but the active principle which mediates an analogous *hormonal* effect expressed in all pterygote insects has been tentatively identified as the terpene alcohol farnesol (fig. 17), or some metabolite closely related to it. Farnesol, and, more effectively, the methyl and ethyl ethers derived from it, mimic at very low dilutions all the effects of the juvenile hormone,[75] the biology of which is discussed more fully in Chapter 9. Juvenile hormone, which is secreted by the corpora allata, has the effect of suppressing the appearance of adult characters during the larval moults. Its absence at the time of the final moult makes possible the full expression of the genes which control adult form.

Defensive secretions

The production of defensive secretions is widespread in insects, and the substances which have been adapted to this purpose are varied.[59]   In addition to the compounds to be considered in this section, which may be grouped rather loosely under the general heading of substances related chemically to the aliphatic compounds of the cuticular wax, quinones play an important part in chemical defence (see Chapter 6), as well as some simpler compounds such as nitrous and hydrocyanic acids. Formic acid, the first member of the fatty acid series, celebrates in its name its importance as the major component of the chemical defences of ants, some of which produce the acid in enormous quantities (up to 20 per cent. of the body weight).   Acetic acid, also, has found a rôle in chemical defence, being part of the secretion of larvae of the moth *Dicranura vinula*.   Hydrocarbon derivatives of slightly higher molecular weight are used by many insects.   Unsaturated aldehydes, in particular, are responsible for the unpleasant odour of many plant-feeding bugs, and are found also in the secretions of cockroaches and ants.   Common constituents of hemipteran stink glands are *trans*-hex-2-enal and *trans*-dec-2-enal, but all the unsaturated aldehydes in the series with from three to ten carbon atoms have been recorded, and in some species the saturated aldehyde *n*-hexanal is the main component.   An unsaturated ketoaldehyde, 4-ketohex-2-enal,

$$CH_3 . CH_2 . \overset{\overset{\displaystyle O}{\|}}{C} . C = \overset{\overset{\displaystyle H}{|}}{\underset{\displaystyle H}{C}} . CHO,$$

is an important constituent of the secretion of the bug *Nezara viridula*.   The reactive aldehydes are usually accompanied by the paraffin *n*-tridecane.   Although the paraffin has no defensive function itself, it may aid the penetration of the active component through the cuticle of a predator, and also prolong its action. Hexenal is also secreted by several cockroaches, and by the African ant *Crematogaster africana*.   The soil-burrowing bug *Scaptocoris divergans* secretes a whole series of unpleasant substances, which have been tentatively identified as all the unsaturated aldehydes of from three to eight carbon atoms, the saturated aldehyde propanol, furans (see below) and quinones.   Observation has shown that the aldehyde solutions are more than mere repellents, especially when used against an arthropod foe. They are squirted on to or rubbed on to the cuticle of the attacker and soon succeed in producing marked symptoms of intoxication. Insects which produce such poisons are immune to their effects, because of the impermeability of their own cuticles. It is not known what chemical difference is responsible for this impermeability, but in the Hemiptera the property apparently resides in the cement layer of the cuticular wax. Sculpturing of the cuticle, especially at vulnerable areas near spiracles may give further protection against penetration of the poison.

The practice of emitting unpleasant fluids is well developed among the carabid beetles, many of which make use of quinones in defence. In several species, however, the defensive secretions of the pygidial glands contain two unsaturated branched-chain acids, methacrylic acid,

$$CH_2 = \underset{\underset{\textstyle CH_3}{\displaystyle |}}{C} . COOH,$$

and tiglic acid,

$$CH_3 . CH = C \overset{\displaystyle COOH}{\underset{\displaystyle CH_3}{\big<}} .$$

These same acids, along with formic and acetic acids, are secreted from the ventral thoracic defensive glands of caterpillars of the moth *Dicranura vinula*.

Several of the defensive secretions of ants have already been mentioned, since in many cases they may be indistinguishable from the trail-marking odours. Several of the dolichoderine ants which secrete methylheptenone and other ketones also produce cyclic compounds of a terpene nature. Two closely related terpenoid dialdehydes have been extracted from different species of ants and have been named iridodial and dolichodial (fig. 17). These compounds probably have toxic effects in themselves, but in addition iridodial tends to polymerize in air, giving a sticky consistency to the secretion, thereby promoting its adherence to predators and prolonging the toxic affects of the more volatile constituents. It is assumed that these compounds are secreted by the anal glands, but so far they have been identified only in extracts of whole ants. A similar terpenoid, with a lactone structure, named iridomyrmecin, has been extracted from the anal glands of the ant *Iridomyrmex humilis*. This terpenoid has insecticidal properties. Extracts of another ant, *Myrmecaria natalensis*, yield an unsubstituted terpene, limonene (fig. 17), the source and function of which are unknown. The defensive mechanism of the ant *Acanthomyops claviger* involves the use of the secretions of two different glands. The mandibular glands eject on to the surface of a foe seized in the mandibles a mixture of citronellal and citral in the ratio of 9:1, while the anal glands spray formic acid from the tip of the abdomen. Besides having insecticidal properties itself, the citronellal greatly aids the penetration of formic acid through the cuticle of the enemy. There is no indication, however, that either the citral or citronellal induce any alarm reaction of the kind that is elicited by citral in *Atta sexdens*. Another ant, *Lasius* (*Dendrolasius*) *fuliginosus*, seems to have a similar double armament. In this species the mandibular gland secretes a terpenoid with a furan ring, named dendrolasin (fig. 17), which is said to be toxic to other ants, but not to insects in general.

Terpenoid defensive secretions are not confined to the ants. The phasmid *Anisomorpha buprestoides* produces a compound which seems to be identical with dolichodial, and the active principle of the defensive liquid ejected by termites of the genus *Nasutitermes* is a mixture of the unsubstituted terpenes α- and β-pinene (fig. 17), which differ from one another in the position of the double bond. Soldiers of *Nasutitermes* defend the nest by squirting on to intruders a stream of liquid from the horn-like frontal organ on the head. The liquid has a purely mechanical action, rapidly coagulating and gumming up the limbs of an enemy to the point of immobilization. This effect is achieved by the polymerization of the terpene. Pinene itself is relatively unreactive, and it is not known by what means polymerization is achieved. The insects may eject a catalyst with the defensive fluid, or the polymer might be preformed in the gland, in which case solidification could result from the evaporation of the monomer after ejection. Finally, the well-known terpene derivative cantharidin (fig. 17), which is the active principle of

' Spanish fly ', a preparation of the dried bodies of beetles of several species of the family Meloidae, is probably also to be included in the list of insect defensive substances, but more is known of the uses of this compound in the social biology of man than of beetles.

Insects, which as far as we know do not possess a mechanism for the production of antibodies, apparently rely to a large extent on chemical agents for protection against pathogens. The hydrocarbon derivatives of the cuticular wax have antibiotic properties, and probably form an effective barrier against invasion of the body by bacteria and fungi. A number of the defensive substances mentioned earlier in this section also have a bactericidal action and may offer some protection against pathogens as well as against predators. The 10-hydroxydecenoic acid of larval bee food, in particular, seems to be concerned primarily with antisepsis. Recently some compounds have been identified in termite blood which also seem to be primarily antibiotic in function, and although they are not related chemically to the compounds mentioned so far, it is convenient to include them in this discussion. Three similar compounds, named nasutins A, B and C, have been isolated from the blood of termites of the genus *Nasutitermes*.[48] They are aromatic substances closely related to ellagic acid (fig. 18), which is found in wood, and it might be supposed that they had been derived directly from ellagic acid absorbed from the diet.

Such a derivation, however, would involve the removal of hydroxyl groups from phenolic residues, a reaction rarely, if ever, found in nature, so it seems that synthesis either *de novo* or from a precursor by the termites or their symbiotes may be more plausible.

When one comes to consider the biosynthesis of the hydrocarbon

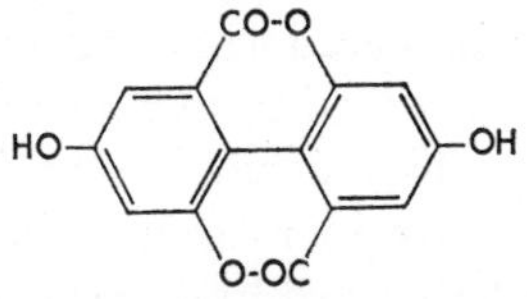

Nasutin A

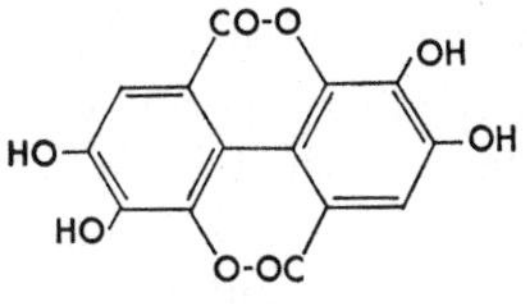

Ellagic acid

FIG. 18. Nasutin A from the blood of termites, and the plant product ellagic acid. Nasutins B and C have structures similar to that of ellagic acid except that two or more hydroxyl groups are methylated.

derivatives with special physiological functions in insects one finds that the information available is very scanty. So far, efforts have concentrated more on identifying the wide range of chemical compounds present in insects than in examining their metabolism. On the basis of chemical and probable biochemical relationships it is possible to classify all of the compounds except the nasutins into two major groups. On the one hand are the straight-chain compounds which can be considered to be derived biologically from fatty acids; on the other hand are the branched-chain and cyclic compounds, which have a common chemical relationship in that they are built up from, or can be derived formally from, five-carbon isoprene units. The second group might embrace such relatively simple compounds as *iso*-amyl-acetate and methylheptenone, as well as the terpenes and their derivatives, which are poly-isoprenoid compounds, two isoprenes forming a monoterpene, three a sesqui-, four a diterpene and so on.

Although the derivation of the straight-chain hydrocarbon derivatives from fatty acids seems fairly obvious, what little evidence there is on biosynthesis is contradictory. Thus some incorporation of labelled acetate into the aldehydes of the defensive secretion of the green vegetable bug has been demonstrated, but other experiments failed to show any conversion of either acetate or stearate to 10-hydroxydecanoate by worker bees. On the other hand, worker bees fed uniformly carbon-labelled sucrose transfer the label rapidly to the decenoic acid. Although these experiments are inconclusive in themselves, they emphasize the wisdom of preserving an open mind about possible synthetic pathways.

The formation of isoprenoid derivatives has been studied mostly in relation to sterol synthesis, and since sterols are not synthesized by insects, the field has received little attention from insect biochemists. The pathway, which is illustrated in figure 19, involves the condensation of acetate units to form mevalonic acid, which is converted into the isoprene donor *iso*-pent-3-enyl pyrophosphate. Terpenes are formed by the condensation of isopentenyl pyrophosphate units. The smallest of these to have been isolated in *in vitro* studies is the sesquiterpenoid farnesyl pyrophosphate, but presumably a monoterpenoid geranyl derivative could be formed by an appropriate enzyme. It is known that insects incorporate mevalonic acid into farnesol and farnesal, so the pathway outlined above is probably the one employed by insects in terpene synthesis. But this indicates, at best, the bare outlines of the synthetic route, and it is obvious that many enzymes must participate in the formation of the large array of substituted and cyclic terpenoids found in insects. The study of the transformations they effect constitutes an unexplored field of inquiry of great importance in the metabolism of insects.

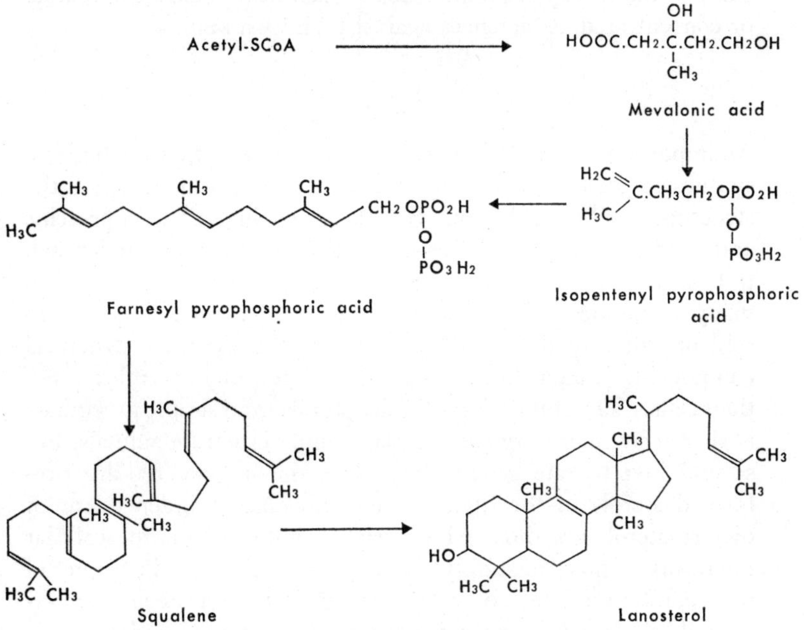

FIG. 19. Biosynthesis of terpenoids and steroids.

Insects depend on their food for a supply of sterols, and it is possible that some of the isoprenoid compounds studied in this section could have arisen from the degradation of sterols. Moreover, several of the terpenoid defensive compounds, such as geraniol, citral, limonene and pinene, are identical with plant products, and have not been recognized in any other animal. This might suggest that the compounds are obtained directly from the diet, and simply concentrated by the defensive glands. But the wide range of terpenoids found, and the fact that they occur in

M.I.—H

insects of widely differing feeding habits, argue against this hypothesis, and suggest that they are, in fact, synthesized from simple precursors. Confirmation of this would provide a further illustration of the similarities in the synthetic mechanisms of plants and insects. It is intriguing also to consider that several of the agents that man has obtained from plants and used against insects, for example, citronella oil and pyrethrum extracts, contain compounds closely related to those which insects have elaborated, or concentrated, as defences against their own kind.

Steroids

An important biochemical peculiarity of insects is their inability to synthesize sterols, which are indispensable components of the structure of all animal cells. Sterols are conjugated with proteins and compound lipids, in chemical relationships as yet undefined, to form the lipoprotein membranes which perform and control so many of the metabolic functions of the cell. Insects thus have to rely on their food for at least two of the essential structural components (choline and sterols) of the lipoprotein membranes of their cells. The ability to synthesize sterols from simple precursors is shared by micro-organisms, plants and vertebrate animals, but several invertebrate groups, including the insects, require pre-formed sterols in the diet.[15] The only insects independent of dietary sterols are those which rely on intestinal or intracellular micro-organisms to supply their needs. A very low rate of incorporation of labelled acetate into cholesterol has been demonstrated in *Blattella germanica*, even when it is reared under aseptic conditions, and a somewhat higher rate of incorporation has been found in primitive apterygote insects. Although absolute proof that this generation of cholesterol is the responsibility of the tissues of the insects rather than their symbiotes has not yet been offered, nevertheless these examples may illustrate the partial survival of a synthetic mechanism possessed by the archetype of the insects. It is known that insects can synthesize farnesol from acetate, so the block in the pathway of sterol synthesis (fig. 19) apparently occurs at some stage after the formation of farnesyl pyrophosphate.

The common sterol of the tissues of animals is cholesterol,

which differs in the structure of its side chain from the plant sterols, of which the commonest is β-sitosterol, and from ergosterol, the major sterol of micro-organisms (fig. 20). As insects rely on their diet for sterols, and since cholesterol is commonly found in insects, it is apparent that they are capable of some modification of the sterols absorbed from their food. On the other hand, some insects have become adapted to a diet containing sterols other than cholesterol, in that they are capable of incorporating such sterols into the structural lipids of their cells. Thus the tissues of the honeybee contain appreciable quantities of 24-methylene cholesterol, which is the principal sterol of pollen, and the Colorado potato beetle is reported to incorporate β-sitosterol directly into its lipid structure without conversion. Similarly, insects reared on an artificial diet containing unusual sterols may either convert such sterols to cholesterol or, in some instances, incorporate them unchanged into their tissues. Such incorporation suggests that the chemical structure of the sterol of the lipoprotein membranes may be varied within fairly narrow limits without harmful effect to the insect. The ability to convert other sterols to cholesterol is developed to varying degrees. Most phytophagous insects are capable of converting the plant sterols to cholesterol; other insects, such as *Musca* and *Calliphora*, have

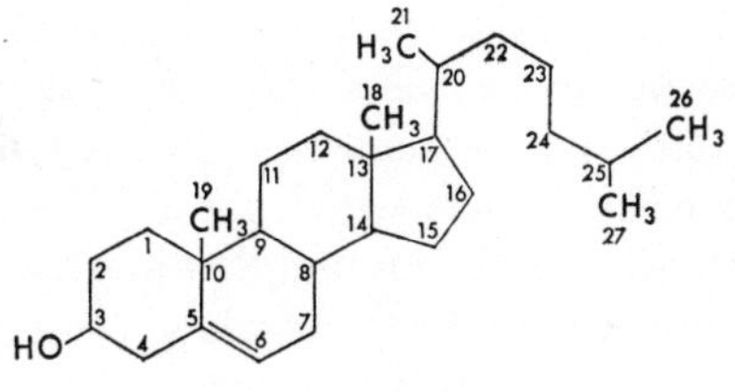

Cholesterol

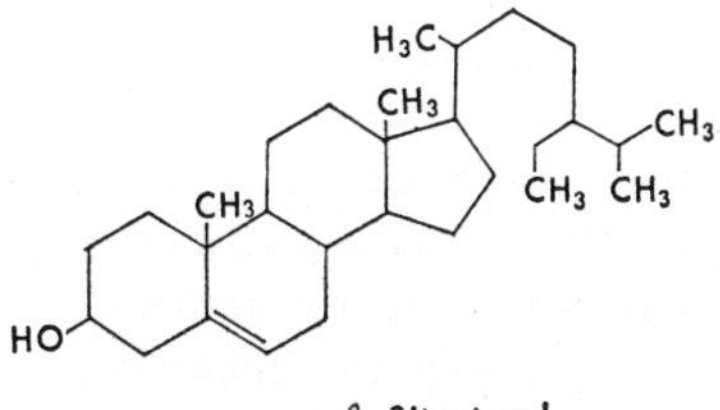

β-Sitosterol

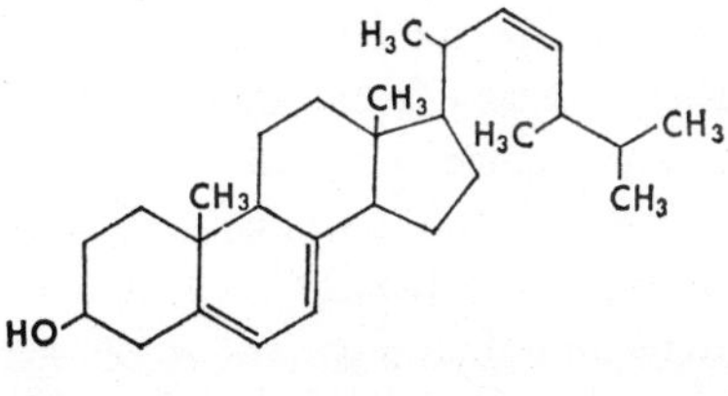

Ergosterol

FIG. 20. Steroids in insect metabolism.

only a low rate of conversion, whereas some which feed only on animal products, such as *Dermestes* and *Attagenus*, are incapable of performing the conversion. The cockroach, *Blattella germanica*, converts the ergosterol elaborated by its intestinal flora to 22-dehydrocholesterol, but seems to be incapable of the further conversion to cholesterol. Although a large proportion of the sterol requirement may be met by sterols other than cholesterol, even in insects which are unable to carry out the conversion to cholesterol, it is found that in such insects there is a small residual requirement for sterol which can only be met by cholesterol. It is thought that this absolute requirement for cholesterol is needed to satisfy the metabolic functions of sterols in insects, as distinct from their ' structural ' function as components of membranes, which has been considered up to this point. Although the so-called ' structural ' function may turn out to be ' metabolic ' when the rôle of the sterols in the membranes is better understood, it seems that the overall size and shape of the sterol molecule may be more important than chemical specificity in this function, and that it is only in the more specific metabolic rôle that absolute chemical configuration is vital. The part played by the steroid hormones in controlling the metabolism and morphogenesis of mammals is well known, but the metabolic functions of sterols in insects are less certain. The moulting hormone, ecdysone, is believed to be a steroid, and it is known that it can be derived metabolically from cholesterol. The brain hormone may also be a steroid, since some commercial samples of cholesterol can mimic its action. So it seems likely that steroid hormones are also active in insects, although their chemical identities still remain to be determined.

Carotenoids

The carotenoids, which, like the terpenes, are isoprene derivatives, constitute one of the major groups of pigments responsible for the body colours of insects.[27] The colours they produce are predominatly yellow, orange and red, but include also blue and violet. They may be classified into two main groups, the carotenes, which are unsubstituted tetraterpenes occurring naturally in the form of three isomers (α, β and γ), and the xanthophylls, which contain

oxygen, and are oxidized derivatives of the carotenes. Carotenoids are synthesized probably only by plants and micro-
organisms, so that insects, like other animals, must derive their
supply from their food. The carotenoids of insects, which include
both carotenes and xanthophylls, occur usually as protein
conjugates. One of the commonest of such pigments, called
insectoverdin, is responsible for the green colour of the blood of
many insects. It appears to be a protein conjugated with two
chromophores, one of which is the yellow β-carotene (fig. 21), and

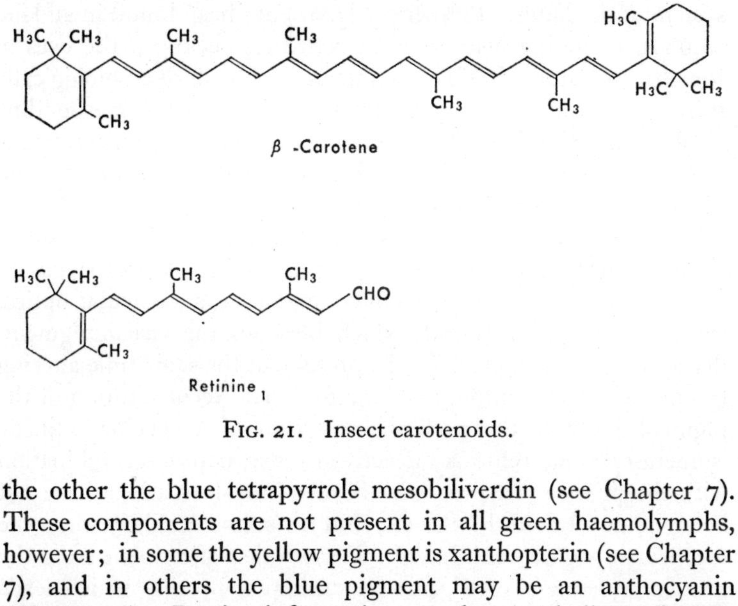

β -Carotene

Retinine $_1$

FIG. 21.   Insect carotenoids.

the other the blue tetrapyrrole mesobiliverdin (see Chapter 7).
These components are not present in all green haemolymphs,
however; in some the yellow pigment is xanthopterin (see Chapter
7), and in others the blue pigment may be an anthocyanin
(Chapter 3). Precise information on the metabolism of caro-
tenoid pigments in insects is very scanty. Their deposition is
clearly under the control of the nucleus, but modification of the
basic morphological pattern is possible in some insects which
undertake so-called ' morphological ' (as opposed to physiological)
colour changes in response to changes in colour of the environment. Such changes are apparently induced by altering the rate
or direction of pigment metabolism, but the metabolic mechanisms
involved are quite unknown.

     In spite of the wide distribution of carotenoids in living

organisms no basic function in the metabolism of cells has been assigned to them. Their main biological rôle seems to be that of photochemical transducers. This may be of importance in photosynthesis in plants, and is certainly the basis of the photo-tactic responses of both plants and animals. In addition, the chromophores of the visual pigments of animals seem to be, without exception, derivatives of carotene. Two diterpenoid aldehydes have been identified as components of the visual pigments of animals. These are retinene$_1$ and retinene$_2$, which differ from one another only by the presence of a second double bond in the ring system of the latter. Retinene$_1$ (fig. 21) has been found in all land animals, including insects, while retinene$_2$ occurs in the eyes of some fresh water fish. The retinenes may be derived biologically from β-carotene, or more directly from their corresponding alcohols, the vitamins A. Although it is some years since retinene was first demonstrated in the heads of insects, efforts to find vitamin A have only recently met with success. It is now known that vitamin A is reversibly converted to retinene in the head of the honeybee by the action of an NAD-linked dehydrogenase.[26] The visual pigments are protein conjugates of a particular optical isomer of retinene. Light, which bleaches the visual pigment, dissociates the retinene from the protein, at the same time altering the molecular configuration of the former. Reconstitution of the pigment requires the preliminary action of a specific retinene isomerase, which reforms the active isomer, before recombination with the protein can proceed. Similar transformations have not been demonstrated in insects, but it seems unlikely that the mechanism would be different. Dissociation of retinene from the protein in some way triggers an excitation process which leads eventually to the production of a nerve impulse from the light-sensitive cell.

The visual sensitivity of insects probably varies widely from species to species, but the more highly evolved flying insects are known to be sensitive to a wave length band which extends into the near ultraviolet, and is thus broader than that perceived by mammals. The honeybee can see light ranging in wave length from at least 3000 to 6500 Å. Physiological experiments have suggested that the compound eye of the honeybee may contain three photosensitive pigments with differing spectral sensitivities within the range of wave lengths perceived by the insect. One such visual pigment has been isolated and found to have an absorption maximum corresponding with one of the maximal points of spectral sensitivity of the honeybee eye. It comprises retinene$_1$ conjugated with a water-soluble protein in a complex which is bleached and dissociated by the action of light. Possibly the other pigments also contain retinene$_1$, combined with different specific proteins, but their constitution has not been determined. The identification of visual pigments other than carotenoids has not been accomplished, although the suspicion remains that others may be present. Thus the housefly still responds to light even after it has been reared for ten generations on a diet free from vitamin A, when retinene can no longer be detected in its head.[17]

For many years neither vitamin A nor the carotenoids from which it may be derived were thought to be essential nutrients for insects, but more recent work has established that the desert locust, at least, requires β-carotene in the diet. Locusts reared on a diet lacking carotene suffer general metabolic defects as well as a lack of pigmentation. The identification of retinene as the visual chromophore of insects of several orders suggests that carotenoids may be required in small amounts in the diets of all insects, but no additional rôle in metabolism, apart from the production of visual pigments, has yet been ascribed to vitamin A in either vertebrates or invertebrates.

5: Metabolism of Insecticides

Although insecticides are not natural objects of insect metabolism, the efforts of man to eliminate his insect competitors in commercial enterprises have become so intense that insecticides can be considered almost constant environmental hazards for some species. Insects, with their capacity for rapid reproduction, have responded to this challenge by the multiplication of selected resistant strains. The need to understand the biochemical basis of such resistance, in order to give direction to attempts to circumvent it, has stimulated a great deal of research on the metabolism of insecticides, some of which will be considered in this chapter. It will not be possible to do justice to the tremendous literature on the subject, and this account will be restricted to describing some general principles, where these seem to have emerged.

Many different mechanisms for the detoxication of potentially harmful foreign molecules exist in insects. They include hydrolysis, hydroxylation, sulphation, methylation, acetylation and conjugation with glucose, glucuronic acid and glycine.[65] Such mechanisms have been studied mostly in relation to the detoxication of compounds of low insecticidal activity, because of the convenience of the analytical methods involved. It is probable however that they play a part also in the detoxication of the more complex insecticides. Several detoxication mechanisms found in insects are quite similar to those found in vertebrates. Thus benzoic acid is converted to its glycine conjugate, hippuric acid, by both groups. Insects, like mammals, also conjugate phenols with glucuronic acid, but this reaction is much less important than

conjugation with glucose (see Chapter 3), a mechanism characteristic of plants and rarely met with in other animals.   Other
mechanisms involved in the detoxication of phenols include
conjugation with sulphuric acid and with acetylated cysteine.
Aromatic amino compounds are commonly acetylated before
elimination. Lipid-soluble compounds must be rendered water-
soluble before they can be eliminated in the urine, and hydroxylation is an important mechanism for achieving this.   Thus
naphthalene is converted to naphthol by a microsomal enzyme
system in the housefly, as a preliminary to conjugation with
several of the metabolites mentioned above.[3]

After this general introduction on the methods of detoxication,
we proceed now to a consideration of the metabolism of the
important members of the synthetic organic insecticides.

The Chlorinated Hydrocarbons

The first of the successful synthetic insecticides, and the first to
which insects developed resistance, was DDT (1,1,1-trichloro-
2,2-*bis*-(*p*-chlorophenyl)-ethane).   Several factors may be involved
in DDT resistance, and they may vary in importance from
species to species or strain to strain.[8]   They include, for instance,
alterations in the permeability of the cuticle to the insecticide and
changes in the efficiency of storage of the
toxicant in sites remote from its point of
action. The most important single factor
in establishing resistance, however, is the
appearance in resistant strains of large
amounts of an enzyme capable of converting

DDT

DDT to its less toxic dichloro-ethylene derivative, DDE.   The enzyme which performs this dehydrochlorination is activated by reduced glutathione, but the degree of resistance to DDT poisoning
in different strains is not related to the glutathione content, or to
the ratio of oxidized to reduced glutathione.   The natural substrate
and function of the enzyme, which is present in very small
amounts in susceptible strains, are unknown.   Some increase in
toxicity of DDT to resistant insects can be achieved by mixing the
insecticide with DDT analogues which may have little insecticidal
action in themselves.   These compounds exert their synergistic

effect by competing with DDT for position on the detoxicating enzyme.

DDT is degraded in vertebrate tissue to the dichlorophenyl-acetic acid derivative by a mechanism which is not known to occur in insects. In resistant strains of *Drosophila* the metabolism of DDT involves hydroxylation rather than dehydrochlorination, the relatively non-toxic derivative being the ethanol analogue, known as kelthane.

Benzene hexachloride, which is a chlorinated cyclohexane derivative, is also dechlorinated in insect tissues, to form pentachloro-cyclohexane. The enzyme which performs this reaction is not the same as the DDT dehydrochlorinase, however, nor is pentachloro-cyclohexane the main metabolic derivative of the insecticide. Both resistant and susceptible insects metabolize benzene hexachloride to water-soluble compounds, although at differing rates. These water-soluble derivatives yield dichlorothio-phenols on hydrolysis, so it seems that conjugation with a sulphydryl compound may be an important part of the detoxication mechanism.

Activation of the insecticide by the metabolism of the insect's tissues is encountered in the chlorinated hydrocarbon group. Thus the polycyclic chlorinated hydrocarbon, aldrin, is converted to its more toxic epoxide, dieldrin, in insects. Although selection of resistant strains by these insecticides occurs, no specific detoxication reactions are known.

The mode of action of the chlorinated hydrocarbon insecticides has not been established, although the signs of poisoning they produce indicate that the nervous system is affected. They apparently do not produce their effect by the inhibition of any known enzyme. Being hydrophobic compounds, they rapidly become associated with lipids in the body, and it is possible that they enter and disorient the lipoprotein membranes which are responsible for ion transport in the nervous system and elsewhere. An effect of benzene hexachloride on the inositol phospholipids of cell membranes has already been discussed (see Chapter 4).

Organophosphorus Insecticides

The organophosphorus insecticides owe their toxicity to inhibition of the enzyme acetylcholine esterase, which has a vital rôle in the maintenance of nerve activity, removing acetylcholine released in the passage of an impulse across synapses and possibly also along axons (see Chapter 2). Many different organophosphorus insecticides of varying complexity have been synthesized; basically their structure is that of substituted esters of phosphate or pyrophosphate, but they may contain P=S, P—S—, P—N= or P—F bonds.[52] They attack the active site of acetylcholine esterase, each forming a relatively stable covalently-linked phosphorylated enzyme. Some agents are known which can dephosphorylate the enzyme, restoring its original activity, and these have been developed as antidotes to the poisons.

In addition to the cholinesterases, animal cells contain a number of other carboxyesterases of varying and often quite wide specificity. They have been classified as aliesterases, enzymes which split principally esters of straight-chain aliphatic alcohols, and arylesterases, which split principally phenol esters, although the substrate preferences of some enzymes may extend into both groups. Although the arylesterases are fairly resistant to organophosphates, the aliesterases are strongly inhibited by the insecticides. In fact, for some time it was argued that the insecticides owed their toxicity to this action, since in some insects aliesterases were inhibited more strongly than cholinesterases, but it is now generally agreed that the significant inhibition is that of the acetylcholine esterase.

Some aliesterases not only bind the toxic phosphate esters at their active sites, but are also capable of carrying out their hydrolysis. Phosphatases also play a part in the degradation of the organophosphorus insecticides. Those compounds with a phenyl ester linkage, such as parathion, may also be hydrolysed to some extent by the arylesterases. The phosphorus-containing residues resulting from such hydrolyses are mostly anionic and can no longer bind to the active site of acetylcholine esterase. Ester hydrolysis is thus an effective means of detoxication, and the aliesterases and phosphatases, in particular, have been implicated in mechanisms of resistance. The action of these two enzymes is illustrated by the degradation of malathion and its more toxic product malaoxon by the mosquito *Culex tarsalis*[47] (fig. 22). In malathion-resistant strains of the mosquito both enzymes have an enhanced activity, but hydrolysis by the aliesterase is responsible for the greater part of the increased tolerance to the insecticide. Potentiation of the insecticide action against such resistant strains can be achieved by adding a number of substituted phosphate compounds, such as tri-*iso*-propyl phosphate, which are non-toxic towards the susceptible strain, but, by inhibiting the carboxy-esterase, prevent destruction of the insecticide in the resistant individuals.

Strains of the housefly which are resistant to the phosphoro-thionate ($\equiv P = S$) insecticides, parathion, diazinon and mala-thion, have a greatly reduced aliesterase activity (as measured by

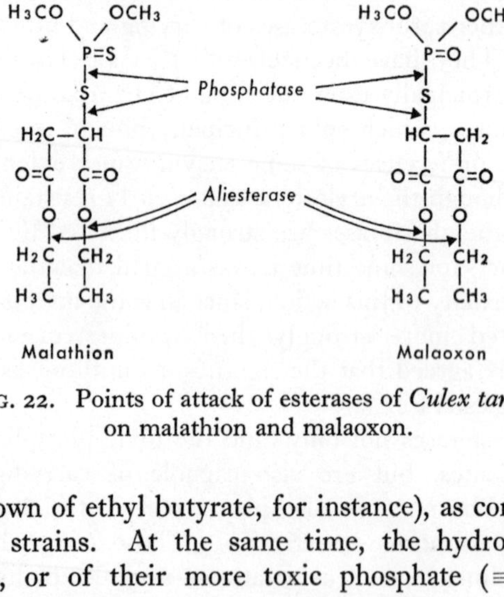

FIG. 22. Points of attack of esterases of *Culex tarsalis* on malathion and malaoxon.

the breakdown of ethyl butyrate, for instance), as compared with susceptible strains. At the same time, the hydrolysis of the insecticides, or of their more toxic phosphate ($\equiv P = O$) or

$$\overset{O}{\underset{\|}{}}$$

thiophosphate ($=P-S-$) analogues, by an enzyme with the characteristics of a phosphatase is much more rapid in the resistant strains. This enzyme is phosphorylated by the insecticides, but the compound formed is less stable than that produced with the aliesterase of the susceptible form, so that the enzyme is slowly restored and the insecticides hydrolysed. Resistance in this species is apparently the result of the mutation of a single gene, which controls the synthesis of an aliesterase. The mutant allele sponsors the production of a slightly altered enzyme protein, which no longer acts as an aliesterase, but as a phosphatase, with sufficient activity against the toxic phosphate esters to render them innocuous.

Enzymes from insect tissues catalyse the oxidative activation of the phosphorothionate and phosphoroamidate insecticides. In the case of the phosphorothionates, the product of activation is the phosphate (or thiophosphate) analogue, whereas phosphoroamidate activation leads to the production of an hydroxymethyl derivative. These oxidized products are much more effective anti-cholinesterases than are the original compounds. Fat body and gut are the most active tissues in phosphorothionate oxidation by insects, and fat body seems to be particularly active in the hydroxylation of phosphoroamidates. Little is known about the mechanism of these oxygenations, but it has been found that the hydroxylation of phosphoroamidates requires both oxygen and an electron donor in the form of $NADPH_2$.

In some phosphorothionate insecticides which contain also a thioether ($\equiv C-S-C\equiv$) linkage (e.g. phorate), the significant reaction in activation is the oxidation of the sulphur of the thioether residue to the sulphoxide or sulphone. The phosphate analogue of phorate has a high anti-cholinesterase activity, but in some insects, at least, seems to be much more rapidly hydrolysed than the sulphoxide or sulphone.

Carbamates

The carbamates, which make up the third important group of modern insecticides, are substituted esters of carbamic acid, having

$$\begin{matrix} R' & O \\ \diagdown & \| \\ & N.C-O-R''' \\ \diagup & \\ R'' & \end{matrix}$$

the general formula   . They are cholinesterase

inhibitors, but the inhibition they produce, unlike that induced by the organophosphorus insecticides, is slowly reversible. Carbamates also inhibit aliesterases, but not arylesterases.

They are metabolized quite rapidly in some insects, but not a great deal is known of the pathways involved, nor have the metabolic products been positively identified. Indications are that both hydrolytic and oxidative mechanisms are involved in the degradation.

6 : Metabolism of Amino Acids

General Metabolism of Amino Acids

The presence of a high concentration and wide variety of amino acids in the blood is a characteristic feature of insects.[77] As far as we know, the concentration of amino acids is not under metabolic control; it varies with the nutritional state, and with the metabolic activities of different tissues. This lack of control may be more apparent than real; for instance, the concentration of proline, which acts as a mobile energy store in the tsetse fly, may be maintained just as closely by hormonal action as is the trehalose concentration of other insects. In many respects, however, the blood seems to act merely as a convenient store for accumulating metabolites. Thus tyrosine normally builds up during larval feeding until the time of moulting, when it is used as the source of the phenolic tanning agents in the formation of the new cuticle. Silk production in the silkworm makes big demands on amino acids of the blood, which may be incorporated directly into the silk protein, or contribute their amino groups to the synthesis of specific amino acids formed for this purpose. Direct accumulation in the blood of amino acids from the diet is seen in several insects in which the blood contains unusual amino acids of plant origin. Thus S-methylcysteine is found in the blood of *Prodenia* when the insect is fed on kale, which contains quantities of the sulphoxide of this amino acid. Similarly, the α-aminobutyric acid found in several species probably comes from the plant food, although this compound can also arise by the degradation of methionine.

All of the amino acids commonly found in proteins have been

identified in insects' blood, although some, such as methionine, cyst(e)ine, serine, hydroxyproline and tryptophan, are found in only a few insects, or in low concentration. Other amino compounds found in the blood include β-alanine and γ-aminobutyric acid, which may have special functions in the central nervous system, ornithine, which is involved in the urea cycle, taurine, which is quite common, but for which no metabolic rôle has been assigned, a number of derivatives of tyrosine and tryptophan, and the amides glutamine and asparagine. Of the two enantiomorphs of the α-amino acids, the L series is by far the commonest in insects, as it is generally in nature, but members of the D series do occur in the free state in insects. D-Alanine is found in the blood of the milkweed bug, *Oncopeltus fasciatus*, and D-serine occurs in several lepidopterous larvae, being present in an amount approximately equal to that of L-serine in the blood of the silkworm.[66] Whether these D-amino acids have any physiological function is not known, but they are apparently not derived from the diet, and are presumably synthesized either by the insects or their symbiotes.

Amino acids may account for an appreciable part of the nitrogen excretion of some insects. This is a particular feature of the excretion of the plant-sucking bugs, the diet of which contains many free amino acids in solution, but smaller amounts of amino acids are present in the excreta of several species. The clothes moth, *Tineola*, excretes large quantities of cystine when fed on wool, a process which may be concerned more with the removal of excess sulphur in the diet than of excess nitrogen. Free amino acids are also present in the saliva of plant-sucking bugs, the seminal plasma of the honeybee, and in some defensive secretions and insect venoms.

Insects require the same ten amino acids in their diet as are essential for mammals. These are arginine, histidine, isoleucine, leucine, lysine, methionine, phenylalanine, threonine, tryptophan and valine. Some unusual nutritional needs have also been reported, of which the best established seems to be that for the simplest of the amino acids, glycine, in members of the Diptera.

Transamination, the transfer of amino groups between α-amino and α-keto acids, has been well studied in insects.[41] As in other animals, the most active transaminase is that which transfers an amino group from glutamate to oxaloacetate, or in the reverse direction, from aspartate to α-ketoglutarate, viz.:

$$\begin{array}{cccc}
\text{COOH} & \text{COOH} & \text{COOH} & \text{COOH} \\
| & | & | & | \\
(\text{CH}_2)_2 & \text{CH}_2 & (\text{CH}_2)_2 & \text{CH}_2 \\
| & | \quad + & | & | \quad + \\
\text{CHNH}_2 & \text{C}=\text{O} \quad \rightleftharpoons & \text{C}=\text{O} & \text{CHNH}_2 \\
| & | & | & | \\
\text{COOH} & \text{COOH} & \text{COOH} & \text{COOH} \\
\text{glutamic} & \text{oxaloacetic} & \text{α-ketoglutaric} & \text{aspartic} \\
\text{acid} & \text{acid} & \text{acid} & \text{acid}
\end{array}$$

A number of other transaminases catalyse the transfer of amino groups from several amino acids to α-ketoglutarate, and conversely the amination of the α-keto counterparts of these amino acids by glutamate. Apart from the glutamate-aspartate reaction, the most active transamination is that between glutamate and pyruvate to form alanine. Rates for the other amino acids are lower. The main route for amino group transfer is through glutamic acid, and direct transfer between other amino acids is less important, although enzymes have been identified in insects which catalyse transamination between alanine and leucine, and alanine and glycine. Glutamic and aspartic acids, and their amide derivatives glutamine and asparagine, which can also contribute their α-amino groups to transaminase reactions, therefore have a central rôle in amino acid metabolism as reservoirs of transferable amino groups. A key compound in transamination is pyridoxal phosphate, which is bound to the enzyme and accepts the amino group to become pyridoxamine phosphate. Pyridoxine is a vitamin for insects, as it is for vertebrate animals.

The main centres of transamination in the cell are the mitochondria, although the glutamate-aspartate and glutamate-alanine reactions have also been demonstrated in the cytoplasm. Fat body is one of the most active tissues in amino group transfer, but activity is also high in the malpighian tubules, where it is probably involved in the process of nitrogen excretion. The muscles of some species are also sites of rapid amino group transfer.

Insect tissues contain enzymes which deaminate amino acids to keto acids and ammonia. These include the amino acid oxidases, which are flavoprotein enzymes capable of transferring

M.I.—I

hydrogen directly to oxygen, with the production of hydrogen peroxide. The reactions catalysed by these enzymes are believed to involve the intermediate formation of imino ($=NH$) compounds, which are rapidly hydrolysed to yield the keto acid and ammonia. As in other animals, the activity of the D-amino acid oxidase is much greater than that which acts on the L-amino acids, if, indeed, an L-amino acid oxidase exists in insects. The true function of the D-amino acid oxidase is not known. Perhaps it exists solely as a mechanism for degrading unwanted D-amino acids, and it may be significant that it is apparently not active in *Oncopeltus*, which contains D-alanine in the blood. The most active enzyme in oxidative deamination in insects is the mitochondrial glutamic acid dehydrogenase, which transfers electrons from glutamic acid to NAD. The reaction, like that catalysed by the flavoprotein deaminases, involves the formation of an intermediate imino acid, which is hydrolysed to α-ketoglutaric acid and ammonia. The $NADH_2$ formed is reoxidized by electron flow through the cytochrome system to oxygen. The oxidative deamination of glutamic acid is thus an energy-yielding reaction, and, of course, the α-ketoglutaric acid formed can enter the citric acid cycle and be catabolized further. Cooperation between the glutamic acid dehydrogenase and the transaminases of the mitochondria can result in the oxidative deamination of probably all the L-α-amino acids. The existence of this system has made it difficult to prove whether insects possess a flavoprotein L-amino acid oxidase comparable with their D-amino acid oxidase. Such enzymes have been isolated from other animals, but no comparable work has been done with insects.

The ammonia cleaved from amino acids is excreted by insects mostly in the form of uric acid, the synthesis of which will be considered in the next chapter. Urea synthesis, which will be discussed later, also has some significance in nitrogen excretion, but a few insects, such as aquatic larvae and blowfly larvae, excrete ammonia directly. It is not known whether the ammonia is cleaved directly from amino acids or whether special nitrogen carriers are involved. It has been suggested that the active adenosine deaminase of the malpighian tubules of blowfly larvae may have a rôle in ammonia excretion, but the complete mechanism has not been worked out.

Metabolism of Individual Amino Acids

Glycine, serine and formate metabolism

The amino acids glycine and serine have an important rôle in the metabolism of single carbon compounds at the oxidation level of formate. A key reaction in the pathway for the entry of single carbon compounds into the carbon skeletons of many cell constituents is the condensation of formate with glycine to form serine. A cofactor in this reaction, and probably in all reactions involving the transfer of formyl and hydroxymethyl groups is tetrahydropteroylglutamic acid, a derivative of the vitamin folic acid. Another vitamin derivative, pyridoxal phosphate, is also concerned in the conversion of glycine to serine. The reaction is reversible, and serine thus becomes a source of the single carbon compounds needed in many biosynthetic processes. The condensation of formate with glycine to form serine has been demonstrated in *in vitro* experiments with insect fat body.

Glycine and serine metabolism are particularly important in the silk gland of *Bombyx*, as these two amino acids make up a large part of the silk protein. Several pathways for the synthesis of the amino acids in the silk gland tissue have been uncovered. Glycine is formed by transamination from glyoxylic acid, which is present in high concentration in silkworm blood. Alanine is particularly effective as amino group donor in this reaction, with glutamate and aspartate next in order of effectiveness. Glycine may also be derived from threonine, presumably by removal of a two-carbon unit. A third pathway of glycine synthesis involves the decarboxylation of aminomalonic acid by an enzyme which was first discovered in the silk gland,[49] but is now known to occur in lower amounts in other animal tissues. Aminomalonic acid is formed, in turn, from ketomalonic acid by transamination. Alanine is also the most effective amino donor for this reaction, although glutamate, asparatate, and α-aminobutyrate are also capable of transferring amino groups to the keto acid. The origin of the ketomalonic acid is obscure; it could be formed from the plant product hydroxymalonic acid, but there may be other pathways. An important intermediate in the formation of serine in the silk gland is 3-phosphohydroxypyruvate. This compound is derived from 3-phosphoglycerate by the action of a dehydrogenase which requires NAD. The dehydrogenase, which was first studied in detail in the silk gland tissue,[42] is obviously a key enzyme in the formation of serine from carbohydrate. Presumably the amino groups required for serine synthesis are derived by transamination

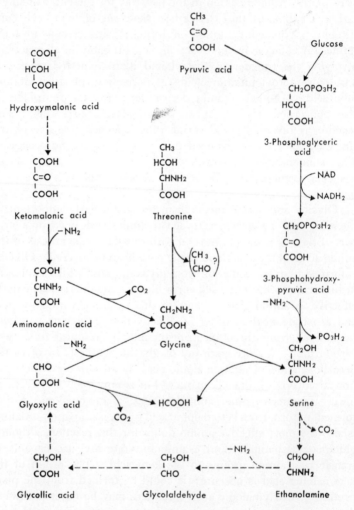

FIG. 23. Glycine and serine metabolism in the silk gland of *Bombyx*.

from the glutamic and aspartic acids of the blood, which are known to be important donors of nitrogen for the silk protein. These pathways of glycine and serine metabolism are illustrated in figure 23. Some additional reactions included in this figure have not been investigated in insects, but their existence is inferred both by analogy with the known pathways of glycine metabolism in other animals and from evidence that the second carbon atom of pyruvate can be converted into either of the two carbon atoms of the glycine of the silk protein.[7]

An aspect of the metabolism of single carbon compounds which is of particular interest in insect biology is the synthesis and storage of the high concentration of formic acid found in the venoms or defensive secretions of many ants. Presumably such formic acid could be derived from serine, but there are many other possible routes, and so far no information exists on the formate metabolism of the venom glands. Not only is the pathway of formation of interest, but also the mechanism by which the tissue is able to secrete and store such a potent cellular poison.

There is some indication that the metabolism of single carbon compounds at the oxidation level of formate is impaired in the Diptera. Nutritional studies have shown that both glycine and either purines or nucleic acids are essential nutrients, or at least growth-promoting substances, in several members of the order. Formate is a necessary precursor in the biosynthesis of the purine ring, so both nutritional requirements support the conclusion that formate metabolism may be unusually dependent on a supply of preformed metabolites. Homogenates of the larvae of the blowfly *Phormia regina* oxidize formate to carbon dioxide.[1] This reaction is catalysed by a peroxidase and depends on a supply of hydrogen peroxide, which can be arranged by coupling the process with the reoxidation of a reduced flavoprotein enzyme (see Chapter 1). Oxidation of formate may have some function in this species as a means of getting rid of formate in a situation where the pathways for its further metabolism are absent or reduced. It is to be noted that *Phormia* is one fly that does not have a nutritional need for glycine, which in this species may be derivable from carbohydrate through serine, a process which would involve formate formation.

Metabolism of the sulphur amino acids: transmethylation

Methionine is related metabolically to a number of compounds, such as choline and betaine, which are concerned in the transfer of labile methyl groups. Present knowledge suggests that the coenzyme S-adenosyl methionine is the principal donor of methyl groups in the cell. Such labile methyl groups are needed in the biosynthesis of many compounds, as, for instance, in the stepwise methylation of phosphatidylethanolamine to phosphatidylcholine. Probably the main mechanism for the remethylation of the S-adenosyl homocysteine formed by the loss of a methyl group from S-adenosyl methionine is the synthesis *de novo* of methyl groups in the cell. Such methyl groups are derived from N_5-methyltetrahydrofolate, a coenzyme formed by the reduction of the folic acid derivatives which arise in the conversion of serine to glycine, or by conjugation of folic acid with formate or formaldehyde. In general, the *de novo* synthesis of methyl groups in animals is too slow to satisfy the demand, and an external source of such groups is needed in the diet. Since methyl group transfer is easily accomplished by most animals, several different compounds may satisfy this need. Methionine, which is required in the diet as an essential component of proteins not synthesized by animals, may, if taken in sufficient amount, also satisfy the requirement for labile methyl groups. Alternatively, homocysteine, the demethylated derivative of methionine, may substitute for methionine in the diet of mammals, if an additional source of methyl groups, such as choline, is added. Insects, however, are unusually dependent on external sources of labile methyl groups, since both choline and methionine are required in the diet of all but a few species in which these compounds are synthesized by internal symbiotes. What little evidence there is suggests that insect tissues are capable neither of synthesizing methyl groups *de novo*, nor of forming choline from ethanolamine by transmethylation. Although dimethylethanolamine is of some value as a replacement for choline in the diet of insects, it is apparently not converted to choline but is incorporated into phospholipids as such.[23] Similarly, carnitine, which can replace choline in the diet of *Phormia*, is built into phospholipids not as choline, but as methylcholine. *Phormia* seems to be more capable of metabolizing carnitine and its derivatives than most insects. It can also use γ-butyrobetaine as a replacement for choline in the diet, whereas this deoxy derivative of carnitine inhibits the growth of other insects. It is not known in what form γ-butyrobetaine appears in phospholipids. Most insects can synthesize carnitine, of course, and presumably perform a number of transmethylations in the

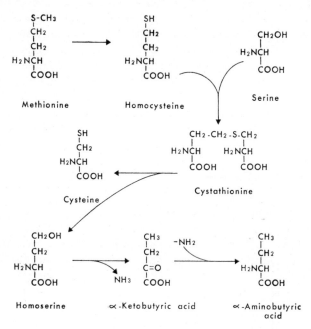

FIG. 24.   Metabolism of methionine.

process, but the methyl groups of carnitine are not transferable to other acceptors. It is in the specific transmethylation of ethanolamine to form choline that insects are deficient.

Methionine is converted to cysteine and cystine by a pathway, illustrated in figure 24, which is usually irreversible in animal tissues. The finding that cysteine can replace methionine in the diet of *Phormia*, however, suggests that reversal is possible in this species, although the mechanism has not been established. The individual steps in the conversion of methionine to cysteine have not been studied in insects, but it is known from isotope work that methionine can give rise to cysteine and α-aminobutyric acid. Cystathionine accumulates in quite high concentration in the blood of the silkworm, and has been shown to be a derivative of methionine in this insect.[43] Apparently the silkworm lacks the enzyme which splits cysteine from cystathionine, which would suggest that cysteine may be an essential nutrient for this species. Although no requirement for cysteine in the diet has been reported for *Bombyx*, *Aedes* has been found to require both cysteine and methionine, so defects in the pathway from methionine to cysteine may not be uncommon in insects. Cysteine can be converted to taurine, presumably by decarboxylation of the oxidized derivative, cysteic acid. Taurine is a common metabolite of invertebrates and is a constituent of one of the phosphagens of annelid muscle, but it has no known function in insects. Another cysteine derivative of unknown function, lanthionine, has been identified in locust muscle.

Several insects, as well as other organisms, possess an enzyme which catalyses the removal of hydrogen sulphide from cysteine, or the cysteine moiety of the tripeptide glutathione, according to the following equation:

$$\begin{array}{ccc} \text{SH} & & \\ | & & \\ \text{CH}_2 & & \text{CH}_3 \\ | & & | \\ \text{H}_2\text{NCH} & \longrightarrow & \text{C}=\text{O} \quad + \quad \text{H}_2\text{S} \quad + \quad \text{NH}_3. \\ | & & | \\ \text{COOH} & & \text{COOH} \end{array}$$

This enzyme is particularly active in the gut of the clothes moth where it may have a dual function of eliminating excess sulphur in the diet of wool, and of maintaining a high concentration of hydrogen sulphide in the gut, thereby ensuring the rapid reductive cleavage of the disulphide linkages of the wool and speeding digestion by the proteolytic enzymes.

The cockroach *Blattella germanica*, and perhaps a few other insects, can live and grow on a diet completely devoid of organic sulphur compounds. They rely for their supplies of methionine and cysteine on the synthetic activities of micro-organisms, which they harbour in large numbers in specialized cells, and which they transmit from generation to generation. The biosynthetic pathway for the formation of cysteine by these symbiotes involves the addition of sulphur to serine. Their synthesis of methionine has not been studied in detail. It is interesting that *Blattella*, although independent of an external supply of methionine, is reported to have a very high requirement for choline for maximum growth, although a few individuals can survive without either methionine or choline in the diet, that is, with no external source of labile methyl groups. This dependence on choline illustrates again the relative ineffectiveness of transmethylation mechanisms in insects as compared with other animals.

Metabolism of glutamic and aspartic acids

The importance of these two amino acids and their amides in transamination has already been mentioned. Free glutamine occurs in high concentration in the blood and tissues of most insects. It is formed from glutamate by a synthetase which is particularly active in larval fat body.[44] This enzyme, which performs the reaction,

$$\text{glutamate} + \text{ATP} + \text{NH}_4^+ \longrightarrow \text{glutamine} + \text{ADP} + \text{phosphate,}$$

also acts as a glutamyl transferase, since compounds other than ammonia can accept the glutamyl residue. The mechanism of asparagine synthesis has not been studied in insects.

Glutamic acid is particularly important in the metabolism of nervous tissue, where enzymes concerned in its conversion are usually found in high concentration. Insect brain contains a glutamic acid decarboxylase, which converts glutamic acid to γ-aminobutyric acid, a neurophysiological agent which seems to be concerned with transmitting the effects of inhibitory neurones.

The β-decarboxylation of aspartic acid to form α-alanine has been achieved in *in vitro* experiments with extracts of the silk gland of *Bombyx*. This may represent an alternate pathway for the synthesis of alanine, which is one of the most important components of the silk protein. Conversion of aspartic acid to α-alanine is known to occur in bacteria, but has not been reported elsewhere in animals. Nothing is known of the biosynthesis of β-alanine, which occurs in the free state in insects.   β-Alanine, like γ-aminobutyric acid is known to depress electrical activity in ganglia of the insect nervous system, and may be one of the transmitter substances of the central nervous system.   It may be synthesized from propionic acid, or could result from the α-decarboxylation of aspartate.

Metabolism of arginine: synthesis of urea

Arginine phosphate is the 'phosphagen' of insects (see Chapter 2), and serves the same function of providing a labile store of phosphate bond energy as that assumed by creatine phosphate in vertebrate muscle.   A specific transferase catalyses the reversible phosphorylation of ADP by arginine phosphate.

Although urea is of minor importance in insects as a vehicle of nitrogen excretion, the majority of species excretes at least some of its nitrogen in this form.   Whether urea is synthesized in insects by the operation of the complete ornithine cycle, which has been established as the mechanism of urea formation in vertebrates, is uncertain.   The enzyme arginase, which cleaves urea from arginine to form ornithine,

$$
\begin{array}{ccc}
\begin{array}{c}
NH_2 \\
| \\
C = NH \\
| \\
NH \\
| \\
(CH_2)_3 \\
| \\
CHNH_2 \\
| \\
COOH \\
\text{arginine}
\end{array}
&
\longrightarrow
\begin{array}{c}
NH_2 \\
| \\
(CH_2)_3 \\
| \\
CHNH_2 \\
| \\
COOH \\
\text{ornithine}
\end{array}
&
+
\begin{array}{c}
NH_2 \\
| \\
C = O, \\
| \\
NH_2 \\
\text{urea}
\end{array}
\end{array}
$$

has been demonstrated in the fat body of some species, but not of others, and both ornithine and urea are known to be present in the haemolymph of some species, but so far there is no evidence that arginine may be reconstituted from ornithine.   The concentration of ornithine in the blood of the tsetse fly increases during starvation, when amino acids are being used as energy sources, but here, also, evidence of a complete ornithine cycle is lacking, and the increase may be simply the result of the catabolism of arginine. It may be that arginase and the small amount of urea excretion for which it is probably responsible are the last remnants of an earlier excretory mechanism now superseded in the uricotelic terrestrial insects.

Putrescine, the decarboxylated derivative of ornithine, has been found in some insects, along with the related polyamine spermidine. Nothing is known of the metabolic significance of these compounds.

Metabolism of tyrosine and phenylalanine

It would be difficult to overemphasize the importance of tyrosine metabolism in insects. Derivatives of tyrosine have an indispensable rôle in the formation of the insect exoskeleton, are responsible for much of the body pigmentation, provide the main components of the chemical defensive armament in some species and probably have a function as chemical mediators in nerve physiology. Insects, in common with other animals, lack the ability to synthesize the conjugated six-carbon benzene ring. Phenylalanine is thus an essential component of the diet. This amino acid may be hydroxylated to form tyrosine, but the reverse process does not occur. In the cockroach *Blattella*, phenolic carbon atoms may be derived from glucose, as well as from aromatic amino acids in the diet, but it may be assumed that symbiotic micro-organisms are responsible for the unusual synthetic ability in this species. The hydroxylation of phenylalanine to tyrosine has not been extensively studied in insects, but the mammalian enzyme has been found to require an electron donor (DH_2) as well as oxygen, the reaction having the form

$$phenylalanine + DH_2 + O_2 \longrightarrow tyrosine + D + H_2O.$$

It is interesting that the natural electron donor is a pterin, and that the dihydro derivative of the sepia pterin of *Drosophila*, which is an intermediate in the formation of the red eye pigment of the fly, and which accumulates in the *sepia* mutant, has an extremely high activity in the mammalian system.[80]

Hardening and darkening of the cuticle. The involvement of tyrosine derivatives in the process of hardening and darkening of the cuticle, which takes place in a period of a few hours after a moult, has been known for more than twenty years. As a result of the efforts of numerous investigators, much information on the chemistry of the cuticular derivatives of tyrosine has accumulated, along with, more recently, some understanding of the enzymatic pathways involved in the hardening process. Insect cuticles vary in hardness from the soft pliable intersegmental membranes, through the tough, flexible cuticles of many larvae to the rigid exoskeleton covering the greater part of the body in many species. Although a degree of continuous growth between moults is possible in insects with flexible cuticles, increase in size is most rapid in the period immediately after the old skin is shed, when the soft newly exposed cuticle is expanded to its full size. In many species, of course, growth is restricted to these periods. Before a moult, the softer parts of the old cuticle are degraded and resorbed while the new cuticle is growing under the remains of the old. The developing cuticle comprises two layers, a thin epicuticle of protein and lipid and a thicker procuticle of protein and chitin. After the moult, the outer region of the procuticle is hardened to a varying degree, thus differentiating the procuticle into two layers, the outer harder exocuticle and the inner softer endocuticle. Hardening is probably always accompanied by some deepening of colour. Most fully hardened cuticles are either dark reddish brown or black, but some of quite light colouration are known. The macroscopic appearance of these cuticles may be due to the incorporation of reflective layers in the cuticle which disguise the intrinsic colour of the cuticular protein, but variation in intrinsic colouration is also possible.

The basic principle that hardening and darkening of the cuticle is the result of the ' tanning ' of cuticular protein by the action of quinones derived from tyrosine was originally proposed as a logical extrapolation from work which established the significance of a polyphenol in the formation of the ootheca in *Blattella*. The sequence of reactions which results in the hardening of the cockroach ootheca has already been described (see Chapter 3). Similar mechanisms for the production of hardened egg cases are found in mantids and locusts. The polyphenol precursor of the tanning agent is protocatechuic acid in *Blattella* and other cockroaches, 3,4-dihydroxyphenylacetic acid in *Locusta migratoria*, and other, but undetermined, compounds in other species. These diphenols are oxidized to highly reactive quinones, which combine with free amino groups (end groups and ε-amino groups of lysine) of the soluble protein secreted by the colleterial gland, causing extensive cross bonding of protein chains, which are thereby converted into a continuous, closely knit structure which excludes water and dries out to form the hard insoluble wall of the ootheca. As far as we know, all insect cuticles harden by an analogous process. The protein component of the endocuticle, secreted in a soluble form, remains hydrated and still partially water soluble (although probably already stabilized to some degree by cross linkage with chitin layers) until the initiation of hardening by the release of polyphenols, or phenolase, or both. Hardening proceeds from the exterior inwards and involves both the epicuticle and the layers which become the exocuticle. The coloured tanned protein formed by quinone action is called sclerotin, and the tanning process is referred to as sclerotization. The enzyme phenolase and several different polyphenols have been identified in insect cuticle. Moreover, it is known that the concentration of free tyrosine in the blood rises before the moult and falls at the time of moulting, and that this tyrosine is incorporated into the insoluble parts of the hardened cuticle. Nevertheless, much of our knowledge of the tanning process is based on inference rather than on a clear demonstration of events in the cuticle, and some details of the enzymatic processes, their sequence, and their control remain obscure.

Although early work established the presence of the hydroxylated derivative of tyrosine (dihydroxyphenylalanine, or ' dopa ') in insect cuticle, subsequent analyses revealed mostly deaminated derivatives of tyrosine. These were dihydroxyphenylpyruvic acid, dihydroxyphenyllactic acid, dihydroxyphenylacetic acid, and dihydroxybenzoic acid (protocatechuic acid). Since these compounds form a logical series derivable from dopa, it was considered that deamination, followed by oxidative decarboxylation or reduction were normal processes in the series of events leading to the release of polyphenols in the cuticle.[28] Such unsubstituted polyphenols as catechol, pyrogallol and even hydroquinone, were also claimed to be constituents of cuticle, and have been proposed as precursors of the tanning quinones. More recent work has established, however, that an amine derivative of tyrosine is implicated in the hardening of the puparium of the blowfly *Calliphora erythrocephala*. In the early stages of the last larval instar of this fly tyrosine metabolism proceeds mainly towards the formation of deaminated derivatives, as a result of the activity of a transaminase which transfers amino groups to α-ketoglutarate. During this period dihydroxyphenylpyruvic and dihydroxyphenylpropionic acids are the major products of tyrosine metabolism. Towards the end of the instar there is a dramatic change in tyrosine metabolism.[37] The deaminated derivatives are now found in only minor quantities, whereas there is an accumulation of N-acetyldopamine, which disappears suddenly at pupation. It has been shown that isotopically labelled N-acetyldopamine, injected into larvae just before pupation, is incorporated into the hardened cuticle of the puparium. Indeed, such incorporation can be followed even if the compound is labelled only in the terminal acetyl group, indicating that the molecule is probably incorporated as a unit, without removal of the side chain. The change in tyrosine metabolism in the blowfly is one of the results of the cyclic production of the moulting hormone ecdysone, secretion of which initiates the whole moulting process.[36] If blowfly larvae are ligated behind the prothoracic gland (incorporated in the ring gland) before the onset of hormone secretion, there is no accumulation of N-acetyldopamine in the posterior half, which is isolated from the gland, but such accumulation can be achieved by the injection of purified hormone.

The pathway of N-acetyldopamine synthesis, which has been the subject of careful study, is illustrated in figure 25. Tyrosine is first hydroxylated by tyrosinase, an enzyme of the phenolase type, to yield dopa. The dopa decarboxylase, which converts dopa to dopamine is dependent on the presence of pyridoxal and iron. It does not decarboxylate tyrosine or tryptophan, but does have some activity against 5-hydroxytryptophan and 5,6-di-hydroxytryptophan. It is inhibited by N-acetyldopamine, which is the next product on the metabolic pathway. The concentration of N-acetyldopamine thus controls the rate of decarboxylation. N-acetyldopamine is formed by acetyl group transfer from acetyl-CoA. The transacetylase catalysing this reaction acetylates tyramine as well as dopamine, but has no action on glucosamine

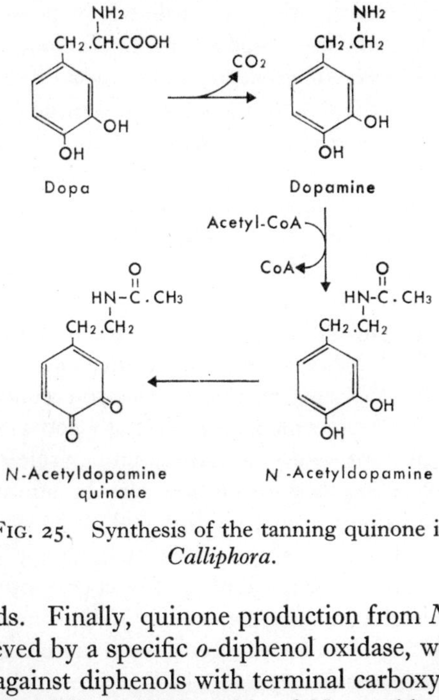

FIG. 25. Synthesis of the tanning quinone in *Calliphora*.

or amino acids. Finally, quinone production from N-acetyldopa-mine is achieved by a specific o-diphenol oxidase, which has only low activity against diphenols with terminal carboxyl groups. At the end of larval life the β-glucoside of N-acetyldopamine makes its appearance in the tissues of the blowfly, but this compound is believed to be a product of excess accumulation of the diphenol with no function in sclerotin formation.

The diphenol oxidase of the blowfly, like other insect phenolases, is present initially in an inactive form, called a pro-enzyme. This is converted to the active enzyme, by a mechanism to be discussed later, as a result of the action of a protein activator, which makes its appearance in the blood at the appropriate time.

Apparently the release of ecdysone from the prothoracic gland induces a rise in the concentration of both the diphenol oxidase and its activator, as well as initiating the production of the dopa decarboxylase. These changes in enzyme concentration, in turn, are responsible for the change in the direction of tyrosine metabolism.

It is apparent that insects contain several different enzymes of the phenolase type, and that a complete understanding of tyrosine metabolism and sclerotin formation will only be possible when they have been isolated and examined in detail. Phenolases are copper-containing enzymes which catalyse the *ortho*-hydroxylation of monophenols and the dehydrogenation of *o*-diphenols. Whether or not these two reactions are promoted at the one enzymatic site is open to question. An enzyme which forms quinones from tyrosine, often known as tyrosinase, is a common constituent of insect blood and tissues. It occurs usually in the form of a pro-enzyme, but destruction of cellular organization, or even exposure of blood to the air, can lead to activation. This enzyme, or group of enzymes, is responsible for the rapid darkening of drawn blood (see later). The hydroxylation of tyrosine, like that of phenyl-alanine, requires the presence of an electron donor, as well as molecular oxygen. Ascorbic acid can act as electron donor for the insect system *in vitro*, and may have a similar rôle *in vivo*. The rate of hydroxylation of tyrosine may also be stimulated by the addition of small amounts of an *o*-diphenol to the system. It may be that the diphenol acts as an electron donor and is itself dehydrogenated to the *o*-quinone in the course of the reaction. Whatever the mechanism may be, it is found that the dehydrogenation of dopa to dopaquinone proceeds much more rapidly than the hydroxylation of tyrosine to dopa. Little attention has been given to the substrate specificity of insect tyrosinases, although it is known that the unsubstituted diphenol catechol is an effective substrate. There is no doubt, however, that these enzymes are distinct from the *o*-diphenol oxidase which catalyses the dehydro-genation of *N*-acetyldopamine in *Calliphora*. Enzymes of both types have been isolated from the blowfly and found to differ widely in substrate specificity. It is not clear, however, in the scheme for sclerotin formation outlined above, why tyrosinase action stops at the level of dopa formation, since dopa is itself such a good substrate for quinone production by the enzyme. Formation of dopaquinone would be expected to lead to the synthesis of the indole pigment melanin, and would divert tyrosine metabolism from the synthesis of *N*-acetyldopamine. Perhaps the activity of the decarboxylase is so high that it effectively removes dopa from the pathway of further oxidation. If this is so, then one would expect activation of tyrosinase also to be subject to hormonal control. Future work may provide answers to these questions.

Several different mechanisms for the activation of the phenolase proenzymes may exist in insects. In some cases activation seems to be the result of the removal of an inhibitor. The activator of the diphenol oxidase of *Calliphora*, however, is an enzyme, apparently of a proteolytic type, since its action can be duplicated by chymotrypsin. A mechanism of activation of the type achieved by this enzyme, which presumably removes part of the proenzyme protein to expose the catalytic site, is not unusual in nature. The activation process in homogenates of *Drosophila* and *Calliphora* is autocatalytic, as if the activation process itself released more activator, although this mechanism is not reproduced in more purified systems. Since more than one phenolase seems to be present in any insect, it is to be expected that multiple activation systems exist, probably with different temporal relationships in the tanning process.

Although the discovery of *N*-acetyldopamine as the tanning agent for the blowfly puparium and the determination of the pathway of its biosynthesis represent tremendous advances in our knowledge of sclerotization, it is not clear just how widely this knowledge can be applied in explaining cuticular hardening in general. Preliminary results have indicated that *N*-acetyldopamine occurs in a beetle, *Tenebrio*, and a locust, *Schistocerca*. On the other hand, sclerotization of insect oothecas clearly calls for the oxidation of different diphenols. Indeed, the specificity of the phenolase from the cockroach colleterial gland is practically the reverse of that of the *Calliphora* enzyme: it acts exclusively on diphenols with a deaminated side chain, oxidizing neither dopa nor dopamine.[73] The ootheca is a specialized structure, however, and its hardening may be expected to present unusual features. But so too is the blowfly puparium a specialized structure: it is formed from the unshed last larval cuticle and is tanned, not immediately after its formation (as in most cuticular tanning), but after its separation from the hypodermis by the newly formed pupal cuticle. Perhaps in other insects the deaminated diphenols identified in the cuticle may have some functional significance. Even in the blowfly the course of sclerotization of the adult cuticle differs in important respects from the events leading to the formation of the puparium. Hardening of the adult cuticle is controlled by a hormone which is produced from neurosecretory cells in the brain and stored in the thoracic ganglion.[21] Production of this hormone is triggered by nerve impulses reaching the brain within a few minutes of the emergence of the adult. The tanning hormone is not ecdysone, nor is it the same as the corpus allatum hormone. Control of tanning at adult emergence is thus quite different from that operating during formation of the puparium. Recent work has shown, however, that the same tanning agent is involved in the hardening of both the adult cuticle and the puparium.

It has been suggested that a process of non-specific hydroxylation of monophenols may play a part in the biosynthesis of tanning agents. Such a process would explain the presence of *para*-diphenols, such as hydroquinone, which have been reported from some cuticles. Hydroxylation of this type might be catalysed by peroxidases, or could even be non-enzymatic. The weight of evidence at the moment, however, suggests that tanning agents are formed by specific enzyme-controlled *ortho*-hydroxylations.

One of the main gaps in our knowledge of sclerotization is the nature of the reaction of the quinones formed by phenolase with the proteins and possibly other components of the soft cuticle. Model experiments have suggested that quinones react with free amino groups to form stable linkages between the nitrogen of the amino group and one of the ring carbons of the quinone. Positions on the ring adjacent to the quinone oxygens are occupied initially but displacement of the oxygens is also possible. Other studies have indicated that the initial reaction of a quinone with protein chains results in reduction of the quinone, so that a diphenol protein is obtained. This is to some extent cross linked and hardened, but is practically colourless. Further oxidation is needed to produce the coloured, completely hardened, quinonoid protein. The existence of a two-step sequence such as this in sclerotization could explain some of the differences in pigmentation of hardened cuticles. Quinones are extremely reactive molecules; they tend to condense with one another in chains or condensed ring systems, all of which are coloured to some extent. It is not clear how important such condensations are in sclerotization, nor how the reactions are controlled. Obviously many possibilities exist—of the formation of condensed systems before reaction with protein chains, of the formation of diphenol proteins at low quinone concentrations, followed by reaction with more quinone to build specific bridges between chains, and so on. Another possibility is that the benzene rings of tyrosine residues of the cuticular protein may be hydroxylated and dehydrogenated *in situ*, a reaction which has also been demonstrated in model experiments. Unfortunately, analyses of the hydrolysis products of sclerotin give little information about the mechanism of cross linkage. The chemical bonds formed by the quinones are so numerous and so stable that hydrolysis yields products which bear little relation to their precursors. Thus hydrolysis of the cockroach ootheca yields no product recognizable as protocatechuic acid over and above the excess protocatechuic acid present in the free state in the ootheca before hydrolysis.[29] One cross linked cuticular protein has yielded identifiable phenolic derivatives on hydrolysis, however. This is the rubber-like protein, called resilin by its discoverer, which is the major component of certain elastic ligaments found in the insect exoskeleton, particularly at the wing bases, where they have an important function in the mechanics of wing movement (see Chapter 8). Resilin owes its rubber-like physical properties to its chemical structure, which is that of long flexible polypeptide chains stabilized by infrequent but regular cross linkages so that it forms a continuous network. It resists solution by any reagent short of one capable of breaking its peptide bonds and degrading it to its individual amino acids. The amino acids resulting from acid hydrolysis of resilin include two fluorescent phenolic compounds, one of which is a diamino, dicarboxylic derivative, the other being triamino and tricarboxylic.[2] The complete chemical structure of these compounds has not yet been worked out. They appear to be the residues of the cross linking quinones, to which are joined the initial amino acid residues of the polypeptide chains (two in one case, three in the other). Probably the infrequency of the quinonoid cross links and their uniformity and relative simplicity in comparison with those of sclerotin have contributed to the successful isolation of these components from the elastic cuticular structures. Resilin is secreted in a single process; it does not undergo secondary modification as does the exocuticle. Thus the process of cross bonding must occur at the moment of secretion. Whether or not some stabilization of this kind occurs during the secretion of the cuticle over the general body surface is yet to be determined.

It must be obvious that the development of the pattern of hard and soft, stiff and elastic, dark and light coloured areas on the apparently uniformly soft and colourless cuticle of a newly emerged insect is the outcome of a closely controlled and highly specific sequence of events, which adheres to a plan laid down by the genetic information. It is not just a matter of pouring out on to the surface a collection of convenient diphenols along with an enzyme of wide specificity. A number of factors can be imagined as the variables from which regulating influences achieve a specific and reproducible effect. They include the nature of the diphenols and the reactive groups on the protein chains, the specificity of the phenolase, the concentrations of all the reactants, and the time sequence of their release. For instance, it is possible that diphenols may be distributed in a pattern throughout the protein before the release of the phenolase, and that the nature of the side chain may play a major part in determining this distribution. Many other possibilities will be apparent to the reader. This branch of insect metabolism has already been a fruitful source of information on the mechanism by which genes attain their morphological expression, and much more remains to be discovered.

Biosynthesis of melanin. Almost all animals make the dark brown or black pigments known as melanins. The initial step in the biosynthetic pathway is the dehydrogenation of dopa to dopaquinone, which is apparently catalysed by the same phenolase as that which induces the formation of dopa from tyrosine. Dopaquinone undergoes spontaneous ring closure and de-carboxylation to form 5,6-dihydroxyindole. Subsequent quinone formation, followed by condensations to form multiple ring systems, apparently occur without the direct intervention of the phenolase. These reactions are secondary oxidations engendered by the presence of an excess of dopaquinone. Melanin formation *in vitro* may be inhibited by the addition of an excess of ascorbic acid, which apparently acts as an electron donor to dopaquinone, reducing it back to the diphenol. This action of ascorbic acid may be of some importance in the metabolic control of tyrosinase activity;

5,6 - Dihydroxyindole

it could be responsible for inhibiting dopaquinone production and encouraging the formation of *N*-acetyldopamine in *Calliphora*, for instance.

Cross reaction with proteins may occur at any point in the polymerization of the indole derivatives, and the end result is usually the production of mixed polymers of very high molecular weight. Melanin occurs in discrete granules in the melanocytes of vertebrates, but in insects the brown and black pigments are usually confined to the cuticle. Such pigments are practically indistinguishable from sclerotin, and it is impossible to determine just how much of the colour of a fully pigmented cuticle derives from pigments of the indole type. The processes of hardening and darkening are to some extent separable in some insect cuticles, however, and there is good reason to believe that at least part of the colour is due to melanin. There is little doubt, either, that the black pigment which forms in drawn blood and homogenates of insect tissue is of the melanin type. If we are to conclude that both melanin formation and sclerotization occur side by side in the hardening cuticle, it is obvious that mechanisms for controlling these two diverging pathways of tyrosine metabolism must be very finely balanced.

Defensive quinones. Quinones and other phenolic compounds are the active constituents of the defensive secretions of many insects[59] (fig. 26). Defence mechanisms based on quinones are particularly well developed in carabid and tenebrionid beetles, but occur also in cockroaches and earwigs. The commonest constituents are *p*-benzoquinone and its methyl and ethyl derivatives. Hydroquinone, which is presumably the precursor of benzoquinone, has also been detected. It is presumed that the quinones are formed at the time of secretion by the action of phenolases. Some beetles are able to eject the quinone secretions of their pygidial glands over considerable distances. This effective method of keeping enemies at a distance reaches its most bizarre development in the bombardier beetles, in which the defensive gland has two compartments, one of which produces diphenols (hydroquinone and methylhydroquinone) and the other hydrogen peroxide. Mixing of these two secretions, presumably in the presence of catalase, induces a violent chemical reaction, the products of which are quinones and oxygen.[62] The rising pressure of oxygen gas then blows out the warm quinone solution in a

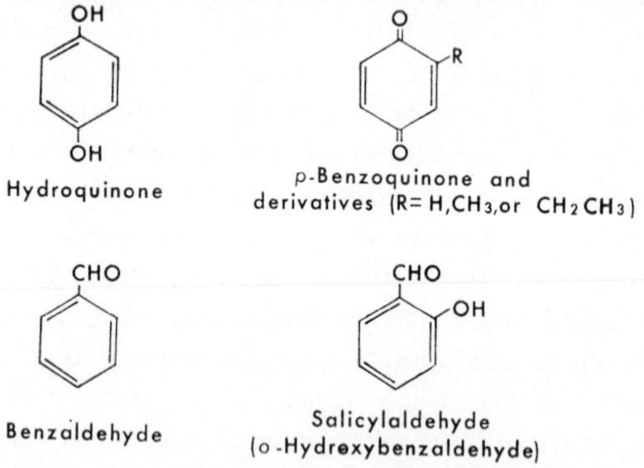

Hydroquinone

p-Benzoquinone and
derivatives (R= H,CH₃,or CH₂CH₃)

Benzaldehyde

Salicylaldehyde
(o-Hydroxybenzaldehyde)

FIG. 26.   Defensive phenol derivatives in insects.

series of audible explosions, which discharge the secretion over the distance of a foot or more, and have a devastating effect on would-be attackers many times the insects' size. In the cockroach *Diploptera punctata*, which secretes quinones from tracheal glands, the diphenol precursors may be stored as glucosides, since the glands contain a β-glucosidase as well as a phenolase. Forcible expiration of air through the spiracles associated with the defensive glands achieves the discharge of the secretion in this species.

The secretions of aquatic dytiscid beetles, which include benzaldehyde and benzoic acid, are thought to have an antibacterial action. They may thus serve an external function similar to that assumed internally by the nasutins of termites. The active component of the defensive secretion of the carabid *Calosoma prominens* is salicylaldehyde (*o*-hydroxybenzaldehyde). The same compound is formed by the larvae of several beetles which feed on willow or poplar leaves, and was believed to be derived from salicin, a product of the trees on which they feed. Salicin is a β-glucoside of o-hydroxybenzylalcohol. *Calisoma prominens* is a carnivorous insect, however, and the occurrence of salicylaldehyde in its defensive glands indicates that insects can synthesize this compound.

The pathways of biosynthesis of the phenolic defensive compounds are quite unexplored. It may be assumed that they are derivatives of phenylalanine and tyrosine, but the location of the hydroxyl residues on the benzene rings suggests that the enzymes responsible for their formation must be quite different from those engaged in the production of tanning agents for the cuticle. Tyrosine is formed by the *para*-hydroxylation of phenylalanine. Further hydroxylation by the phenolases so far studied in insects adds an hydroxyl residue in the *ortho* position to yield 3,4-dihydroxyphenylalanine (dopa). Dopa is the precursor of *ortho*-quinones, but the defensive quinones are *para* isomers. Conversely, *ortho*-hydroxybenzaldehyde would seem to be a derivative of the *ortho*-hydroxylation of phenylalanine (fig. 26). Some support for the possible existence of this last reaction in insects is afforded by the reported occurrence of *ortho*-tyrosine in insects.

Hormone derivatives of tyrosine. Adrenalin and noradrenalin, which are derivatives of dopamine, have been found in insects. Of the two compounds, noradrenaline is quantitatively the most important, and it seems likely that it may act as a transmitter substance in some nerves or neuromuscular junctions, as it does in the vertebrate autonomic nervous system. The corpus cardiacum of insects produces one or more substances of a catecholamine nature which have adrenaline-like activities on vertebrate tissues. They probably include the hormone which controls trehalose concentration in the blood (see Chapter 3). The functions of adrenalin or noradrenalin, or of compounds related to them, thus seem to parallel quite closely in insects their functions in vertebrates. Catecholamine hormones of vertebrates appear to exert their effects primarily by stimulating the formation of the cyclic adenyl compound adenosine-3',5'-phosphate, which in turn may stimulate certain enzymes or influence the transport of ions across membranes. Mechanisms of this nature have not been studied in insects.

Insects are capable of synthesizing 3-monoiodotyrosine, 3,5,3'-triiodothyronine, and thyroxine from injected iodine. Although these compounds are said to stimulate the growth of insects when they are included in the diet, there is no evidence that thyroxine has any metabolic function in the group. Since the iodinated tyrosine derivatives are found mostly in the cuticle, it is possible that they are an accidental result of the occurrence of highly reactive quinones.

Metabolism of tryptophan

The metabolic rôle of tryptophan in insects parallels that of tyrosine in two respects: it is a precursor of an important group of pigments and of hormones with significant, but as yet largely undefined, effects on the nervous system.

Ommochromes. The tryptophan derivatives called ommochromes by their discoverers occur as general body pigments in insects of several orders, being responsible for yellow, red and brown colours.[10] Probably their most important function, however, is that of masking pigments in the compound eye. Pigment granules containing ommochromes are located in the accessory cells of the retinas of the compound eyes of probably all orders of insects. Their presence ensures the optical isolation of the individual ommatidia, and makes possible the formation of a mosaic image by the eye. Ommochrome pigments are also found in the eyes and integument of crustaceans and molluscs.

As general body pigments, the ommochromes are most plentiful in members of the Lepidoptera, where they occur not only in the epidermis and wing scales but also in malpighian tubules, gut, fat body, brain and reproductive organs. Synthesis of ommochromes in the moth *Cerura vinula* begins at the end of larval life and is manifested by the appearance of red areas in the formerly green epidermis. Shortly after this stage, the pigments make their appearance in the gut and fat body. Internal synthesis persists during the pupal period as the organs are changed into their adult form, and is accompanied by the appearance of the pigments in the newly formed epidermis of the adult. Considerable quantities of ommochrome pigments may be excreted into the gut lumen during pupation, and are voided as the so-called ' meconium ' after the emergence of the adult.

The unravelling of the pathway of ommochrome synthesis, which is illustrated in figure 27, was an event of great historical

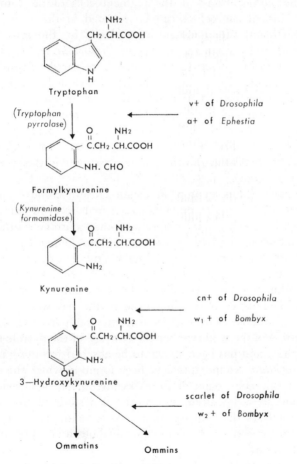

FIG. 27. Pathway of ommochrome synthesis and points of action of genes.

significance in biology, since it was a by-product of the first demonstration of the mechanism of gene action, the concept that genes initiate the synthesis of enzymes, which, in turn, are responsible for specific metabolic reactions. This work was done on identifiable eye-colour mutants of *Ephestia, Drosophila* and later *Bombyx*. Changes in the eye-colour of these mutants are the result of a failure to synthesize the dark brown ommochromes which normally obscure the red or yellow pteridine pigments found with the ommochromes in the pigment cells of the compound eyes. Normal eye colour can be restored in the *v* mutant of *Drosophila* and the *a* mutant of *Ephestia* by the injection of kynurenine. In other mutants (*cn* of *Drosophila*, w_1 of *Bombyx*), the injection of 3-hydroxykynurenine is required to restore the full eye colour. From this it could be concluded, and has subsequently been proved, that both these compounds are on the pathway of ommochrome synthesis. They are not formed in the mutants because of the lack of specific enzymes, the synthesis of which is controlled by the mutated genes. Interruption of tryptophan metabolism in these mutants results in the accumulation of excessive amounts of the precursors of the missing metabolites. Thus tryptophan accumulates in *v* and *a* mutants, kynurenine in *cn* and w_1 mutants, and 3-hydroxykynurenine in w_2 mutants, in which the interruption in ommochrome synthesis is, at a point between 3-hydroxykynurenine and the pigment. These metabolites accumulate in the malpighian tubules, and are excreted in large amounts, especially at adult emergence. So far a causal relationship has been established between only one recognized enzyme and its corresponding gene in the pathway of ommochrome synthesis. This enzyme is tryptophan pyrrolase, which is responsible in the wild type for the cleavage of the pyrrole ring of tryptophan, and has been shown to be absent from the *v* mutant of *Drosophila*. No mutants have been found in which the second reaction, the conversion of formylkynurenine to kynurenine by formamidase, is impaired, and no detailed study of the enzyme which catalyses the hydroxylation of kynurenine has been made. These early reactions of tryptophan metabolism take place mainly in the fat body.

The condensation of two molecules of 3-hydroxykynurenine to form the phenoxazine pigment xanthommatin is a coupled oxidation-reduction which depends on the oxidation of dopa to dopaquinone by phenolase (fig. 28). By acting as electron acceptor, dopaquinone induces firstly the condensation of two molecules of 3-hydroxykynurenine and then the cyclization of one side chain into a quinoline ring. Xanthommatin (fig. 29) is a common eye pigment of insects, and has been found in a wide range of orders. It is also present in the epidermis, wing scales, and internal organs of members of the Lepidoptera. Reduction of the molecule to the unstable dihydro form causes a change in colour from brown to red. A similar change, which occurs naturally in the epidermal pigments of larvae of *Cerura vinula* according to whether the insect is grown at lower or higher temperatures, is believed to be the result of a change in the state of oxidation of the xanthommatin in the epidermis.

Two other phenoxazine pigments have been isolated from

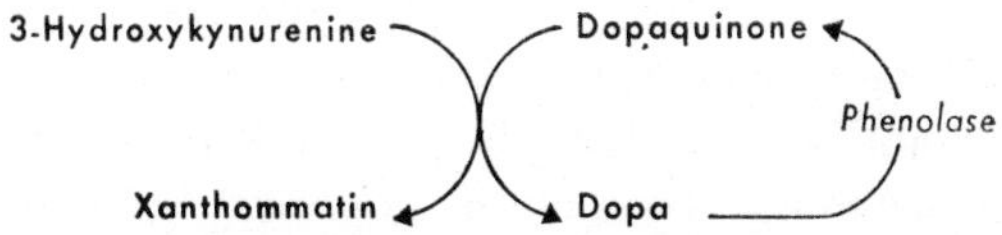

FIG. 28.   Mechanism of xanthommatin synthesis.

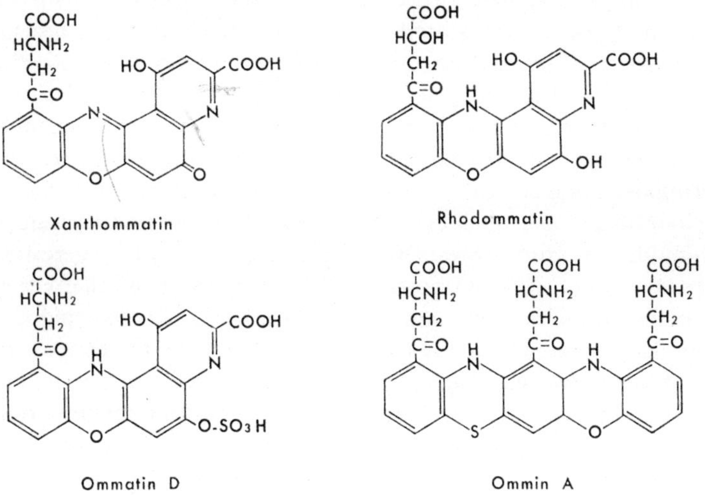

FIG. 29.   Ommochrome pigments.

lepidopteran insects, where they occur in the epidermis and internal organs, but not in the eyes. These are the red rhodommatin, which is stable in the reduced form, and resembles dihydroxanthommatin, except that the amino group of the side chain is replaced by an hydroxyl, and ommatin D, which is a sulphate ester of dihydroxanthommatin (fig. 29). The pigments dealt with so far are the simpler members of the ommochrome group, and have been named ommatins. They sometimes occur in association with pigments of higher molecular weight, which have been distinguished by the name ommins. One of these, isolated from the eye of the silkworm, and called ommin A, is a product of the condensation of three molecules of 3-hydroxykynurenine, and incorporates a sulphur atom (fig. 29).

Ommochromes are apparently always synthesized in association with ribonucleoprotein particles in the cell, in contrast to melanin, which, as we have seen, is essentially a non-particulate pigment of the integument of insects. Formation in granules may be an indication of the mechanism by which the synthesis of these two pigment classes are kept separate, since both pathways are catalyzed, as far as is known, by the one enzyme, phenolase. The condensation of 3-hydroxykynurenine units to form the ommochromes is clearly under genetic control, as mutants have been found in which the synthetic pathway is interrupted at this point, but the genes involved evidently do not control the synthesis of phenolase. They may be responsible for the synthesis of other components of the pigment-forming granule. The simultaneous formation of melanin and ommochromes by the action of phenolase on dopa and 3-hydroxykynurenine has been demonstrated both in model systems and homogenates of insect tissue. The final colour achieved in such experiments has been varied from yellow, through red and brown, to black, according to the relative proportions of tryptophan and tyrosine derivatives in the mixture. Whether there is any condensation together of the two pigment types is unknown. In any case, it seems unlikely, for the reasons mentioned above, that such mixtures occur under natural conditions. Furthermore, the model systems lack an important component of the pigment-forming granules, that is the pteridine derivatives, which are also capable of reversible oxidation-reduction, and which may have a function in the synthetic pathway.

The biology of the pterins will be discussed in the next chapter. *Metabolism of kynurenine.* Kynurenine and 3-hydroxy-kynurenine are extensively metabolized in insects, and a number of their derivatives have been identified (fig. 30). None of the enzymatic steps involved in the metabolism have been studied,

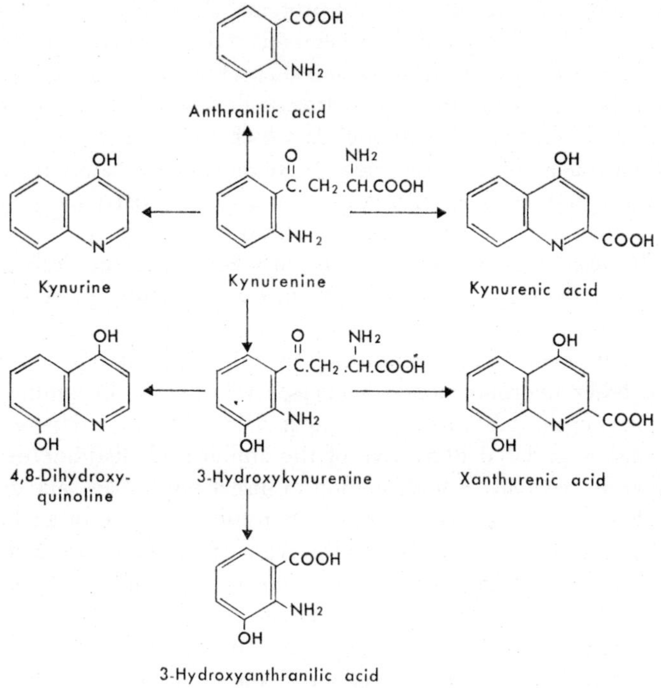

Anthranilic acid

Kynurine   Kynurenine   Kynurenic acid

4,8-Dihydroxy-quinoline   3-Hydroxykynurenine   Xanthurenic acid

3-Hydroxyanthranilic acid

FIG. 30.   Metabolism of kynurenine.

however, and the transformations indicated in figure 30 are inferences based mainly on the existence of similar reactions in other animals. Both compounds lend themselves to quinoline ring formation, probably as a result of the action of transaminases, the deaminated derivatives being kynurenic acid and xanthurenic acid. Kynurine (4-hydroxyquinoline) and 4,8-dihydroxyquinoline are also found in insects, and probably arise by transamination from the decarboxylated derivatives of kynurenine and 3-hydroxy-kynurenine. Removal of alanine from the side chains yields anthranilic acid and 3-hydroxyanthranilic acid. The last compound is a precursor of nicotinic acid in some animals, but this pathway has not been demonstrated in insects, and present evidence suggests that their need for nicotinic acid in the diet cannot be met by increased tryptophan intake. Many, perhaps all, of the enzymes responsible for the reactions illustrated in figure 30 can be expected to be pyridoxal proteins, and, in fact, it has been established that tryptophan metabolism is impaired in insects grown on diets deficient in pyridoxal and that such insects excrete quantities of kynurenine, 3-hydroxykynurenine, kynurenic acid, and xanthurenic acid, compounds which impart a yellow colour to the urine and faeces. Some of these metabolites have a function as body pigments in insects, kynurenine, in particular, being accumulated in the wing scales of pierid butterflies.

Hormone derivatives of tryptophan. Several amine derivatives of tryptophan have functions in insect physiology. Serotonin (5-hydroxytryptamine), a potent vasopressor substance in mammals, occurs in the venoms of several wasps, often in company with other neurohormones, such as acetylcholine, histamine and various peptide and protein activators called ' kinins '.[4] Histamine, the decarboxylated derivative of the amino acid histidine, is not known to have any other function in insect physiology, and so far has been found only in venoms. Serotonin, on the other hand, occurs also in the brain, ventral nerve cord, and corpora cardiaca of insects, where it presumably has a normal physiological function. It is found in quite small concentration as compared with acetylcholine, and may be the product of a few specialized cells. The hydroxylation of tryptophan in insect tissues has not been studied, but neural tissue is known to contain an enzyme capable of decarboxylating 5-hydroxytryptophan.

Other amine derivatives of tryptophan act as hormones or mediators of hormone action in insects. The accessory gland of the male American cockroach secretes an indolealkylamine which induces peristaltic contractions in the female oviduct. The identity of the active compound, which is said to be a dihydroxy derivative, has not been established. It seems not to be 5,6-dihydroxytryptamine. The corpora cardiaca of the same insect secrete a hormone, apparently of a peptide or protein nature, which increases the rate of heartbeat and of peristaltic gut movement.

This hormone acts by stimulating the pericardial or gut cells to secrete an indolealkylamine, which is responsible for the action on the peripheral nervous system. A decarboxylase, which is unmasked or stimulated by the hormone, has been implicated in the production of the amine.[19] Some vertebrate hormones have also been shown to produce their effects by stimulating the production of indolealkylamines in the target organ.

7 : Metabolism of Some N-cyclic Compounds

Metabolism of Purines

Various combined forms of purines and the related pyrimidines have functions of fundamental importance in the metabolism of all living things. The significance of purine and pyrimidine ribosides and riboside phosphates (nucleosides and nucleotides) as coenzymes in a multitude of interactions between all classes of biological compounds and as biological energy transducers has often been mentioned in preceding pages. Later in this chapter an account will be given of the rôle of purines and pyrimidines as constituents of the nucleic acids, compounds which more than any other are to be considered basic to life. But the main function of purines in the free state in insects, and the major concern of this section, is that of vehicles for the excretion of nitrogen. Excretion of nitrogen in the form of uric acid is characteristic of the majority of terrestrial insects, although degradative products of uric acid are minor constituents of the excreta of many species, and are of major significance in some. Since purines are relatively complex molecules and their synthesis requires much more energy than does the formation of simpler excretory products such as urea, it is pertinent to ask what advantage to the organism is to be found in this type of nitrogen excretion. The important feature of uric acid is its low solubility, which means that it can be excreted in a solid form, with a consequent conservation of water by the organism, whereas simpler vehicles of nitrogen excretion, such as urea, and, particularly, ammonia, are quite soluble, and toxic in fairly low concentrations, so that their elimination can only be achieved in a copious and dilute urine. Thus uric acid excretion is found in animals in which water conservation is an overriding need, a category to which most terrestrial insects clearly belong. The low solubility of uric acid also favours its storage in cells or in integumentary adornments such as the feathers of birds or the wing scales of insects, thus providing another means, apart from actual excretion, for the disposal of unwanted nitrogen.

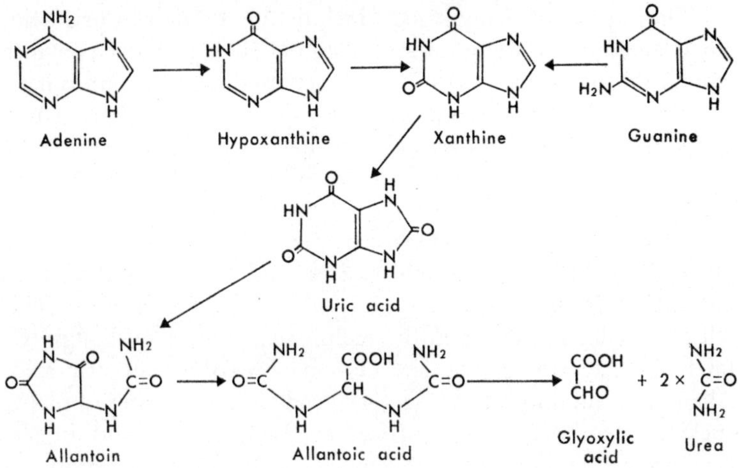

FIG. 31.   Metabolism of uric acid.

Purines are formed, as their ribotides, by a long series of reactions which involve the addition of ammonia, glycine, formate and aspartate to a phosphorylated derivative of ribose. This pathway has not been studied in detail in insects, but what evidence there is suggests that the synthetic mechanism is the same as it is in other animals. Several enzymes which catalyse the inter-conversion of different purines have been identified in insects. These include the deaminases which convert adenine to hypo-xanthine, and guanine to xanthine (fig. 31), as well as the enzyme xanthine oxidase, which oxidizes hypoxanthine to xanthine and xanthine to uric acid, and also has a rôle in pterin metabolism (see below). Xanthine oxidase is apparently involved in the normal

M.I.—L

formation of uric acid as an end product of nitrogen metabolism, since the mutant *rosy* of *Drosophila*, which lacks the enzyme, excretes hypoxanthine in place of uric acid. Thus it seems that the biosynthetic pathway which incorporates the ammonia derived from amino groups does not lead directly to uric acid, but involves the prior formation of other purines. Xanthine and hypoxanthine are normal excretory products in some insects, but whether these species lack xanthine oxidase, or whether conditions are so reducing in their excretory organs as to discourage oxidation, is not known.

The excreta of many insects include, in addition to uric acid, small amounts of allantoin and allantoic acid, and the enzymes responsible for the catabolism of uric acid to these compounds have been recognized in a wide range of species.[57] Uricase, which splits uric acid to allantoin, is particularly widespread in insects, whereas allantoinase, which is responsible for the production of allantoic acid, has a more restricted distribution (fig. 31). Even the enzyme allantoicase, which converts allantoic acid to urea and glyoxylic acid has been recognized in the cricket *Acheta domestica*, although this insect excretes most of its nitrogen as uric acid. All these enzymes occur in the malpighian tubules, although the fat body may also be the site of some breakdown of uric acid. Allantoin is an important excretory product in a number of plant-sucking Hemiptera, in plant-feeding Lepidoptera, and in the carrion-frequenting larvae of blowflies. Allantoin and ammonia account for all the nitrogen excretion of blowfly larvae, which possess an active uricase. This enzyme disappears during the pupal stage and reappears in the adult. Allantoic acid accounts for an appreciable part of the nitrogen excretion in only a few insects, notably in lepidopteran larvae. There seems to be little advantage to be gained for the organism by the performance of these two hydrolytic steps. The appearance of breakdown products of uric acid in the excreta may be an accidental effect of the presence of enzymes of purine metabolism, and the absence of any selective pressure to suppress their activities in the excretory organs of insects living on diets with a high water content.

Uric acid not only acts as the main vehicle for nitrogen excretion in insects; it also constitutes a convenient nitrogen store, often of considerable metabolic significance. This is particularly apparent during metamorphosis, when uric acid stored during larval life may be reworked as a source of nitrogen and carbon in the formation of the adult tissues. The enzymes of uric acid catabolism mentioned above may have some significance in this conversion, although no insect is known to have the full complement of enzymes needed to degrade uric acid nitrogen to the level of ammonia. It is more likely that purines enter such metabolic cycles in the form of ribotides, which may then be metabolized by reversal of some of the steps of purine synthesis. Some evidence to support this idea has been found in the fact that the carbon adjacent to the two nitrogens of the pyrimidine ring of uric acid exchanges more readily with labelled formate than do the other carbons. This carbon is the last to be added in biosynthesis and would be the first to be removed in its reversal.

Isoguarine

Uracil

Cytosine

Thymine

Purines are stored not only in internal organs, but also in epidermal structures, where they may take on a secondary function as pigments. Uric acid, xanthine and hypoxanthine, as well as isoguanine, a purine of rare occurrence in nature, have been identified in the wings of pierid butterflies.

Nucleic Acids

Nucleic acids are polymers of large molecular weight formed from ribotides and deoxyribotides of purines and pyrimidines. Sugar units of only the one type are found in any one nucleic acid, which may thus be classified as either a ribonucleic acid (RNA) or a deoxyribonucleic acid (DNA). As a general rule, DNA occurs only in the nucleus of multicellular organisms, where it is the major constituent of the chromosomes which carry the genetic code. RNA is found both in the nucleus and in the cytoplasm. A major part of the cytoplasmic RNA is in the form of discrete ribonucleoprotein particles which are attached to the endoplasmic reticulum. These so-called ' ribosomes ' are particularly abundant in cells which are engaged in rapid protein synthesis. Nucleic acids are long-chain polynucleotides held together by phosphodiester linkages, the phosphate attached to the 5' position of one sugar unit forming a second ester linkage with the 3' position of the next. In DNA, and perhaps some RNA, the chains are wound around one another in a double helix, with the purine and pyrimidine bases directed in towards the centre of the spiral, the whole being held together by hydrogen bonding between opposing bases. The bases which enter into the formation of RNA are adenine, guanine, uracil and cytosine. Uracil is replaced by thymine in DNA, which also contains varying amounts of 5-methylcytosine.

According to the now well-known theory of Watson and Crick, the spatial relationships within the two-stranded helix of DNA are such that complete bonding is only possible when an adenine residue is opposite a thymine, and a guanine opposite a cytosine. This concept of ' base pairing ' has provided the clue to the unravelling of the mechanism of chromosome replication and the transfer of genetic information to the cytoplasm, and has stimulated a veritable avalanche of research over the last few years. If the two halves of a double-stranded helix of DNA separate, each can act as a template, which, because of the limitations of base pairing, determines the base sequence in a growing DNA polymer. Completion of this process through the whole molecule results in the production of two daughter molecules identical with the parent. If DNA is the genetic material, then this process provides a satisfactory model of chromosome replication. Similarly, if the sequence of bases along a strand of DNA comprises the genetic code for the synthesis of a specific protein by the cytoplasm, then it is conceivable that the uncoiling of a section of the DNA strand could lead to the synthesis of a complementary nucleic acid, which could pass out of the nucleus into the cytoplasm to become a template for the assembly of amino acids in a specific sequence determined by the sequence of bases along the nucleic acid. Experimentation has provided convincing demonstration of the truth of these concepts, and although there remain many questions to be answered, it seems that an explanation in molecular terms of the mechanism of heredity has been realized. RNA, synthesized in the nucleus and passed to the cytoplasm, is the carrier of the genetic code, which resides in the base sequence of the chromosomal DNA. This messenger RNA, which is produced intermittently as particular genes become active, and usually has a short life time in the cytoplasm, becomes associated with the ribosomes or ribonucleoprotein particles derived from them. A third kind of RNA of lower molecular weight, called soluble RNA, combines with free amino acids. A sequence of probably three bases on each soluble RNA molecule comprises a specific label for each amino acid. The assembly of amino acids into the correct sequence for a particular protein is achieved by the matching of the three bases of each aminoacyl-RNA complex with its complementary base triplet on the messenger RNA template. The precise rôle of the ribosomes is unknown, but they are certainly a necessary part of the protein synthesizing mechanism.

Further information on protein synthesis will be given in the next chapter. In this section we are concerned only with what information there is on the composition and metabolism of nucleic acids in insects. DNA isolated from insect material obeys the quantitative limitations of the Watson-Crick model, in that its adenine content is equal, within reasonable limits, to its thymine content, and its guanine to its cytosine. The ratio of adenine plus thymine to guanine plus cytosine varies between $1 \cdot 4$ and $1 \cdot 6$, and is higher than in mammalian DNA's. In insect RNA the ratio of adenine plus uracil to guanine plus cytosine may be more or less than one, and may vary from larval to pupal life, when different sets of genes are active. Synthesis of DNA in the nucleus, and rapid turnover of RNA in the nucleus and accumulation in the cytoplasm have been demonstrated, but nothing is known in insects of the enzymatic processes of nucleic acid synthesis. Insects, like all other cellular organisms, contain active ribonucleases, which split the phosphate ester linkages of RNA.

Pterins

The pterins, or pteridine derivatives, were first discovered in insects. They were isolated as water-soluble pigments from the wings of butterflies and given the name which specifies their origin before their chemical structure was known. They are now recognized as compounds of general importance in cellular metabolism, but of particular significance in insects. As pigments, pterins are responsible for some epidermal colours in Hymenoptera, as well as in the wings of Lepidoptera. They also have a rôle as accessory pigments in insect eyes, where they are associated with ommochromes. Pterins probably occur wherever ommochromes are formed, although their distribution is not restricted to such situations. They produce colours ranging from white, through yellow and orange, to red. Some pterins are colourless, but most fluoresce brilliantly, with colours that cover the whole visible spectrum. Structural formulae of the known insect pterins are shown in figure 32.

The simplest member of the pterins and the compound from which all the other members of the group may be considered to be derived has usually been called 2-amino-4-hydroxypteridine, although modern information suggests that the compound carries a proton on the ring nitrogen rather than on the oxygen atom, and the formula is now written as shown in figure 32. This compound has been extracted from many insects, although some records may be in doubt, since it is easily formed during extraction as a degradation product of the more complex and more labile pterins. Of the water-soluble pigments isolated from the wings of pierid butterflies, the simplest are the yellow xanthopterin and the white leucopterin. Two red pigments from the same source are of more complex structure. One, called pterorhodin,[53] has a double pteridine structure linked by a methylene bridge; the other, named erythropterin, has an acidic side chain on the 7 position. These two red pigments occur also in the eyes of the moth *Ephestia*, where they are accompanied by two other pterins called lepidopterin and ekapterin, which are similar to erythropterin, but have slightly modified side chains. The colourless isoxanthropterin is found in the wings of butterflies and the eyes of moths and flies. Its wide distribution suggests that it may be important in insect metabolism, but no function has been established for it.

The compound eye of *Drosophila* contains a number of pterins, some of which have defied chemical characterization. They include 2-amino-4-hydroxypteridine, xanthopterin, isoxanthopterin, biopterin, two yellow pigments and one or more red

pigments. It is not clear just how many of these compounds are
intermediates on the biosynthetic pathway or degradation
products of the more complex red and yellow pigments, which are
quite labile. The yellow component accumulates in the eyes of a
mutant of *Drosophila* called *sepia* which lacks the red pigment,
suggesting that the latter is derived from the former. Yellow
pigment isolated from the eyes of *sepia* has been found to include

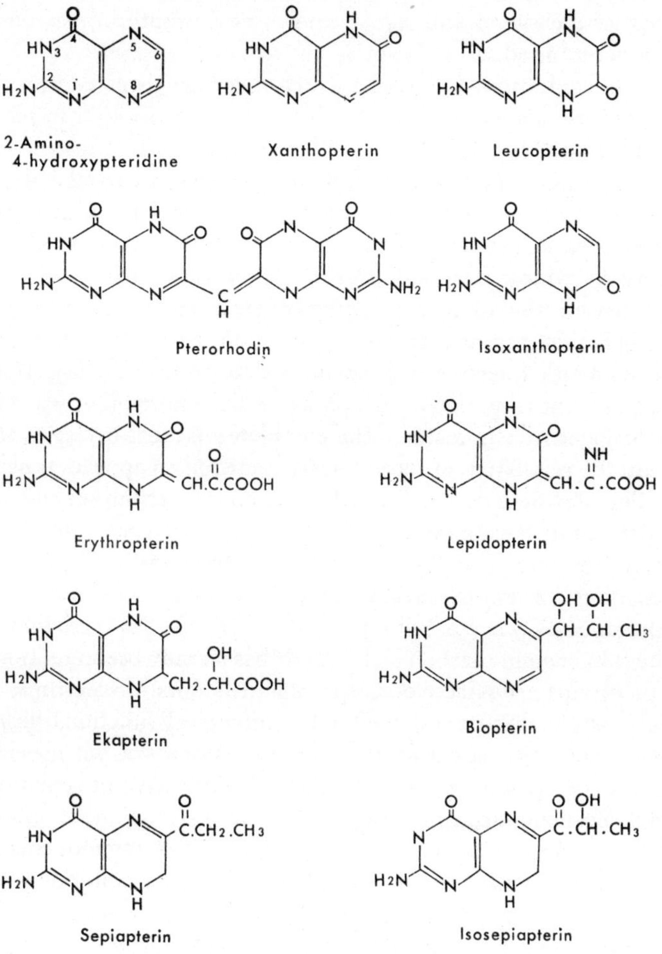

FIG. 32. Insect pterins.

two components: one, called sepiapterin, has a propionyl side chain on the 6 position, the other, called isosepiapterin, has a lactyl residue in the same place.[20] The yellow pigments also occur in the silkworm, which contain an $NADPH_2$-dependent enzyme capable of reducing the yellow sepiapterin to its colourless dihydro derivative. This enzyme is absent from the *lemon* mutant of *Bombyx*, larvae of which acquire a yellow colour as a result of the accumulation of sepiapterin. The structure of the red pterin of the eye of *Drosophila*, known as drosopterin, has not yet been determined.

The compound biopterin, which has been isolated from the eyes of *Drosophila* and *Ephestia*, is of wide distribution in nature, and may have functions in metabolism quite distinct from its rôle as an eye pigment. It is found, for instance, in royal jelly, the special food stored by worker bees in the cells from which future queen bees will emerge, and so far is the only compound to be identified which is found exclusively in these cells and is not included in the diet of future workers. It is not yet known whether this pterin has any connection with the tremendous fertility of the queen, but it has been claimed that the injection of biopterin into nymphs of aphids which normally reproduce parthenogenetically restores the complete bisexual cycle, so some rôle in the regulation of reproductive metabolism appears possible.

The pteridine derivative with the widest distribution and most fundamental metabolic rôle so far recognized is the vitamin pteroylglutamic acid (folic acid), a pterin with a side chain containing *p*-aminobenzoyl and glutamyl residues. The importance of this compound as a coenzyme in the oxidation and reduction of single carbon compounds has already been mentioned. Most pterins are effective acceptors and donors of electrons, and it is possible that one of their main biological functions may be as coenzymes in oxidation-reduction reactions not yet specified. We have already noted that the dihydro derivative of sepiapterin is an excellent electron donor in the hydroxylation of phenylalanine, and it seems likely that the natural coenzyme of this and other hydroxylation reactions will turn out to be pterins. The regular occurrence of pterins in the melanocytes of amphibians and other animals, where melanin is synthesized, may be an indication of such a function. There must also be some significance in the association of ommochromes and pterins, and indications of metabolic interrelations between these two classes of pigment have been provided by studies on eye-colour mutants in insects.[79] Several mutations seem to affect only one class of pigment, but the eyes of a mutant of *Ephestia* which is unable to convert tryptophan to kynurenine lack the pterin ekapterin and accumulate in its place the non-fluorescent dihydro derivative, a fact which suggests a connection between the oxidation of the pterin and the metabolism of the amino acid. Several other genes which influence ommochrome synthesis have an effect on pterins, and vice versa. Thus the white-eyed mutants of several insects have neither class of pigment in the eyes, although simple pterins, which may be eye-pigment precursors, can be detected in the pupae before the emergence of the adult. It has been suggested that absence of eye pigments from the mutants is caused by interference with the production of the granules on which the pigments are normally synthesized. Whether the function of the pterins of the pigment cells is solely that of coenzymes in the reactions of ommochrome synthesis, or whether they have other rôles, are matters of speculation. They are certainly present in amounts which suggest that their function is more than that of coenzymes. Although pterins are particularly prone to modification of structure as a result of the absorption of light energy, and would thus seem to be suitable agents for the transduction of light energy in vision, evidence so far suggests that they are confined, with the ommochromes, to the accessory cells of the compound eye, and have no direct connection with the biochemistry of vision.

The addition of oxygen to the pteridine ring system is catalysed by the enzyme xanthine oxidase, which in insects is more effective in the oxidation of pterins than of purines. This enzyme catalyses the conversion of 2-amino-4-hydroxypteridine to isoxanthopterin and of xanthopterin to leucopterin. The mutant *rosy* of *Drosophila*, which lacks xanthine oxidase, has a depleted pterin complement in the eyes. Isoxanthopterin is absent, while the red eye pigment is reduced. On the other hand, 2-amino-4-hydroxypteridine accumulates in excessive amounts. These data indicate that the enzyme has a rôle in the biosynthesis of the pteridine eye pigments.

Purines are effective precursors of pterins in insects, and it seems likely that the purine ribotide guanosine-5'-phosphate may be a key compound in the synthetic pathway.   Cleavage of the imidazole ring of the nucleotide followed by the formation of a six-membered ring incorporating the first two carbons of the sugar molecule has been suggested as a likely mechanism.   The feeding of possible precursors labelled with radiocarbon to insects has yielded evidence which supports this concept.[6, 64]   It has been established that the carbons shared by both rings are derived from glycine, that carbon 2 comes from formate, and carbon 4 from carbon dioxide.   All these facts are consistent with the known pathway of biosynthesis of the pyrimidine ring of purines. Carbons 6 and 7, on the other hand, are derived from glucose, suggesting that a ribose sugar derived from glucose is their immediate precursor.   If the proposed mechanism is true, then it is likely that the pterin first formed is one with a three-carbon side chain on position 6, a proposition that is also supported by experimental evidence.   Presumably the simpler pterins and those with side chains on carbon 7 are derived by secondary processes.

Pyrroles

The tetrapyrrole nucleus with an associated metal atom comprises the prosthetic group of a number of proteins of universal signific-ance in biology.   These metal-por-phyrins include the cytochromes and haemoglobin, the functions of which have been dealt with in earlier chapters.   The purpose of this section is to mention briefly a pyrrole-protein with a more specialized function in insects as a body pigment.   The chromo-phore of this pigment, which is blue in colour, appears to be the tetrapyrrole mesobiliverdin.   The pyrrole-protein is normally associ-ated with yellow pigments to form a green complex which has been called insectoverdin.   The yellow chromophores vary from species to species: they may be either carotenoids or pterins.

Mesobiliverdin

8 : Protein Metabolism

Structure of some Insect Proteins

A number of insect proteins, particularly structural proteins, are of unusual interest, and will be considered in this section. Some mention has already been made of the structural proteins of the insect cuticle (Chapters 3 and 6). Some of these may be glycoproteins, which either before or at the moment of their deposition, or by subsequent reaction, become covalently linked with the chitin component of the cuticle. The nature of the protein-carbohydrate link is unknown, although analyses of chitin hydrolysates provide evidence that histidyl and aspartyl residues of the protein are involved. Resistance of the cuticle to chemical degradation has so far hindered attempts to isolate a glycoprotein unit, and, in fact, so many secondary reactions are possible in the cuticle that the isolation of such a unit from formed cuticle seems unlikely. On the other hand, controlled enzymic degradation may be expected to yield information on the nature and frequency of the chitin-protein bonds. The soluble proteins which are easily removed from the cuticle show no unusual properties, although their tyrosine content is quite high, a fact which may be significant if tyrosyl residues are oxidized to quinones *in situ* (see Chapter 6).

The unique rubber-like protein which is found in certain elastic cuticular ligaments of insects has also been mentioned briefly. This protein is secreted by the hypodermis, sometimes in almost pure form, but usually in lamellae 2 to 5 μ thick sandwiched between thin (0·2 μ thick) sheets of chitin. In cuticles of this nature there is no evidence of bonding between the chitin and protein components, which are secreted successively by the same cells in a regular rhythm in the growing cuticle. The protein component, which has been named resilin, is cross linked into a continuous network, which, in spite of its hydrated state, is insoluble in any reagents other than those which split its peptide bonds and degrade it into its constituent amino acids. Its properties are consistent with a model of a three-dimensional isotropic network of hydrated flexible polypeptide chains subject to thermal agitation. Chains are held by a few stable cross links, between which they have complete rotational freedom. Deformation of such a network leads to a change in entropy, but almost no alteration in the internal energy of the chains. Recovery is complete when the deforming force is removed. Resilin, in fact, approaches more closely an ideal entropic rubber than any other natural or synthetic compound, a property which fits it for its rôle as a fatigueless and largely frictionless hinge between the more solid working parts in the articulation of the wing, or as an elastic component which stores energy during one part of the cycle of wing movement and releases it at another.[71] The isolation from hydrolysates of resilin of phenolic compounds containing either two or three amino groups (see Chapter 6) suggests that cross linkage of the protein chains may be achieved by reaction with a quinone. This reaction probably takes place on the cell surface as the protein is deposited, and in view of the infrequency and regularity of the cross links must be a specific and closely regulated process.

Different cuticular areas in insects exhibit a considerable variation in elasticity, and it is probable that resilin is a component of a number of such areas. Indeed, it has been suggested that the range in elasticity of cuticles could be explained by the co-existence of the cross-linked protein resilin, which is poor in tyrosine and may not be capable of being tanned by the cuticular tanning agents, and a protein rich in tyrosine, which is originally water-soluble but is subsequently tanned to a resin-like material, these two protein types occurring in layers separate from the semi-crystalline sheets of chitin.[35] Further work will be needed to test the validity of this concept, which runs counter to earlier ideas of rigid tanned protein-chitin complexes. So far resilin is known only from the small elastic structures.

A number of insects secrete silks, which they fabricate into nests or cocoons for the protection of the pupa. Silk is produced from modified labial glands in some insects, from modified malpighian tubules in others, and from dermal glands opening on various parts of the body in a number of species. The silk of *Bombyx*, which is the best known and commercially most important of insect silks, contains two components: an amorphous protein or mixture of proteins called sericin, within which is embedded a pair of continuous fibres of the insoluble semi-crystalline protein fibroin. These two proteins differ widely in amino acid composition. Sericin is mostly remarkable for its high content of serine, which is usually a minor amino acid of proteins. Serine was first identified as a protein amino acid in hydrolysates of sericin, in which it is the major component. *Bombyx* fibroin also has an unusual amino acid composition in the great preponderance of the simpler amino acids glycine and alanine, which together comprise about 75 per cent. of the total number of amino acid residues.[40] Serine and tyrosine make up about another 15 per cent., and these four amino acids are probably the sole constituents of the crystalline part of fibroin, the remaining amino acids being confined to the smaller amorphous region. Formation of the rigid semi-crystalline fibres is probably a spontaneous process which occurs as the viscous protein mixture formed in the silk glands is forced through the small orifice of the spinnaret. The fibroin threads produced from the two glands remain separate but the sericin components mix together. The sericin, which is secreted in a water-soluble form, later dries out to form an insoluble glue surrounding the fibres. The amino acid compositions of fibroins secreted by several insects have been determined, and although they vary quite widely all agree in their high content of the simpler amino acids, glycine, alanine and serine.

Some of the protein components of insect venoms have strange and powerful pharmacological actions. The proteins of venoms include a number of enzymes, such as phospholipase (see Chapter 4) and hyaluronidase (see Chapter 3), with well documented effects on mammalian tissues, but less well known are the agents which exert toxic and narcotic effect on arthropod victims. Particularly interesting are the components of hymenopteran venom, believed to be of a protein nature, which produce long-lasting paralysis in arthropods captured by the adult female and prepared by her as future nourishment for her larvae.[4] The action of some of these compounds is restricted to only a few species. So far almost nothing is known of their chemistry.

Protein Synthesis

An outline of current concepts of protein synthesis and its control by nucleic acids has already been given. The first step towards the assembly of amino acids in specific sequences in polypeptide chains is the ' activation ' process. This involves the condensation of each amino acid with ATP to form an aminoacyl adenylate and pyrophosphate. The same enzyme which performs this transfer then effects a second transfer of the aminoacyl residue to an RNA molecule of relatively small molecular size, which carries somewhere in its structure the base sequence which is the code for the amino acid. Thus there is a soluble RNA species for each amino acid and also an activating enzyme specific to each amino acid. Assembly of the amino acids in the correct sequence is then achieved by the matching of the code sequences of their soluble RNA conjugates with complementary base sequences on an RNA template to which are attached ribonucleoprotein particles of the cytoplasm. Formation of peptide bonds then occurs by a mechanism as yet unknown. The attachment of amino acids to a growing peptide chain is believed to be a sequential process as the ribosome particles move over the surface of the template RNA.

The posterior part of the silk gland of *Bombyx* is known to produce fibroin, and since this tissue is engaged in the synthesis of a large amount of a single protein of unique structure it offers many advantages as a material for the study of protein synthesis. Several such studies have been made, and the results have not always been in agreement with those based on other animal material. Although activation of amino acids has been demonstrated in silk gland homogenates, the enzymes seem to be to a large extent bound to the particulate material of the cell, which is thus capable of the whole process of incorporation of amino acids into proteins, a process which in mammalian liver is shared between the particulate ribosomes and the soluble activating enzymes. On the other hand, silk gland particles supplied with amino acids and activating enzymes derived from mammalian tissue incorporate amino acids in a pattern characteristic of silk gland protein, rather than the protein of the mammalian cells which supplied the activating enzymes, a fact which is consistent with the concept of templates attached to ribosomes, as outlined above. Moreover the RNA fraction of low molecular weight from the silk gland binds glycine at a very rapid rate, as would be expected in view of the importance of this amino acid in the fibroin molecule. In bacteria and mammalian cells the template, which must have a base structure similar to that of nuclear DNA, since it is the messenger which carries the genetic code to the site of protein synthesis, is turned over very rapidly. While a gene is active RNA is constantly being synthesized and passed out to the cyto-plasm, where it is quickly broken down after acting as the template for probably only a few protein molecules per RNA polymer. Thus RNA synthesis and protein synthesis are seen as proceeding hand in hand. This temporal relationship does not exist in the silk gland. Rapid RNA synthesis occurs in the posterior half of the silk gland during the early part of the last larval instar, at a time when the gland is increasing greatly in size. It is not until the end of the instar that fibroin synthesis is initiated in the posterior half of the gland, and at this time RNA synthesis is practically at a standstill.

Messenger RNA has been isolated by a technique known as ' pulse labelling '. Radioactive phosphate is supplied to a cell, and the newly synthesized RNA into which it has been in-corporated is isolated. Because the turnover of messenger RNA is normally so high, the isolation must be performed within a few minutes of the addition of a single ' pulse ' of labelled intermediate. Investigators using this technique have isolated newly synthesized RNA with a base composition showing obvious relations with the base composition of the DNA of the cell, and differing widely from the base composition of the bulk of the cytoplasmic RNA. This is consistent with the concept of the nuclear origin of RNA templates with base sequences complementary to that of genetic DNA. The technique has been successful in demonstrating the synthesis of RNA resembling DNA in base composition in a developing wing of a moth, but when it is applied to the silk gland during fibroin synthesis no evidence for the formation of messenger RNA is found. On the other hand, pulse labelling does demonstrate the synthesis of an RNA fraction similar in base composition to silk gland DNA at the early phase of silk gland enlargement.[34] This means that if the messenger concept holds for the silk gland the messenger is an unusually stable one, produced during a phase of RNA synthesis long before protein synthesis is started. The fact that the messenger is produced only once, and that its bulk is small in comparison with the bulk of cellular RNA explains why the base composition of the total RNA of the posterior part of silk gland shows no unusual features and is similar to RNA's from the rest of the silkworm body or from other insects, a fact which at first sight would be unexpected in a tissue engaged in the synthesis of a single protein with an overwhelming preponderance of only a few amino acids.

There may be other unusual features in protein synthesis in the silk gland. It has been noticed that the amino acid compositions of fibroins from different species of Lepidoptera may differ rather widely from one another.[5] This is unusual, since homologous proteins from closely related species usually differ in no more than a few amino acid residues. It has been suggested that fibroin synthesis may involve the assembly of preformed polypeptides, rather than of single amino acids, and thus a mutation which might result in the loss of a whole peptide could explain the big differences between species in amino acid composition. So far no evidence in support of this idea has been brought forward.

Protein Catabolism

Insects encounter proteins of many different kinds in their diet and most species are equipped with proteolytic digestive enzymes. The most widely distributed of these enzymes are endopeptidases of the trypsin type with pH optima on the alkaline side of neutrality and properties very similar to those of mammalian trypsin. Digestive mechanisms which involve the secretion of acid along with pepsin-like enzymes operating at very low pH, such as are found in the mammalian stomach, are not known in insects, although enzymes of the pepsin type, with pH optima as low as 2·4 have been demonstrated in a few species. Little work has been done on the specificity of insect exopeptidases, but it is known that *Tenebrio molitor* has a carboxypeptidase which removes C-terminal lysine and arginine residues only, and an amino-tripeptidase which splits leucine from the tripeptide leucyl-glycyl-glycine.

Several insects are capable of digesting fibrous proteins which are unusually resistant to proteolytic attack.[70] Collagen is one such protein. True collagenases, capable of degrading the native protein, are quite rare in the animal kingdom, but the larvae of certain blowflies which live in carrion secrete such an enzyme. Keratin, the fibrous protein of wool, hair and feathers, is also extremely resistant because of its strong cross linkage by covalent disulphide bonds. Yet keratin is the major element of the diet of such insects as the clothes moth and the carpet beetle, which digest it quite successfully. Keratin becomes much less resistant to proteolytic attack if its disulphide bonds are broken, and it was originally suggested that the success of the clothes moth in digesting keratin was due to the extremely reducing conditions it maintained in its gut, which prepared the protein for hydrolysis by an ordinary protease. But when the protease of the clothes moth was eventually isolated and purified, it was found to be a remarkable enzyme capable *in vitro* of degrading a considerable proportion (30 per cent.) of native keratin under anaerobic conditions.[54] Presumably cystine released by this enzyme in the gut of the clothes moth is absorbed by the midgut cells and reduced to cysteine by cystine reductase. Part of the cysteine is thought to be broken down by cysteine desulphydrase, to form hydrogen sulphide. Both cystine reductase and cysteine desulphydrase have been demonstrated in clothes moth larvae, and the gut is known to contain cysteine and hydrogen sulphide when wool is being digested. Cysteine and hydrogen sulphide released from the gut cells promote the cleavage of the disulphide bridges of the keratin, and so accelerate its continued digestion by the protease.

9 : The Control of Metabolism

In the foregoing chapters we have explored, as well as present knowledge and imperfect understanding will allow, the individual processes encountered in the metabolism of insects. Wherever possible, emphasis has been placed on the integration of individual reactions into the regulated pattern of events which we recognize as metabolism. Some intimations of the mechanisms by which metabolism is controlled have also been given in descriptions of specific aspects of metabolism or of chemical control agents. It is the purpose of this chapter to review these control mechanisms in a general way, and to deal more specifically with hormonal controls affecting the metabolism of the whole organism.

Regulation within the Cell

Control of metabolism within the cell is achieved by a variety of means, most of which are common to all cells. In the first place, the structural organization of the cell provides a basis for control, in that spatial isolation or the presence of diffusion barriers may prevent interaction between different parts. We have seen several instances in earlier chapters of metabolic control which is dependent on the segregation of enzymes, or groups of enzymes. Such segregation, for instance, coupled with a characteristic pattern of enzyme concentration, is responsible for some unique features in the energy metabolism of housefly flight muscle (Chapter 1). Regulation may also depend on the existence of separate pathways for the catabolism and biosynthesis of important metabolites.

Activities of individual enzymes or of sequences of enzymic reactions are commonly regulated by the availability of substrate or of coenzymes, or the concentration of reaction products. Respiration, for instance, is controlled, as a general rule, by the availability of substrate, the substrate in this case being the ADP which acts as phosphate acceptor. But in insect flight muscle there is an additional control mechanism hinging on the availability of α-glycerophosphate superimposed on the normal phosphate-acceptor control. In the face of a plentiful supply of ADP, the availability of electron carriers may be the limiting factor in respiration. Thus resting respiration of muscle is relatively insensitive to the effects of cyanide, whereas activity respiration is strongly inhibited, indicating that under these circumstances the concentration of cytochrome a is limiting the respiratory rate. Similarly, in diapause the virtual cessation of demands for ATP results in an extremely low respiratory rate which is insensitive to cyanide poisoning (Chapter 1).

Diapause metabolism also gives us an example of control exercised by competition for a coenzyme. In the phase of active growth which precedes diapause, especially diapause in the egg, there is probably a heavy demand for $NADPH_2$ for biosynthetic reactions. When this demand ceases, a number of enzymes, which may be of only minor significance in normal metabolism, use the accumulating $NADPH_2$ to reduce glycogen to glycerol and sorbitol (see Chapter 1).

Many enzymes are inhibited directly by the accumulation of the products of the reaction they catalyse; others, performing one of a series of transformations, may be inhibited by the products of a reaction one or more steps removed in the sequence. An example of such ' negative feedback ' is seen in the inhibition of dopa decarboxylase by N-acetyldopamine (Chapter 6). Positive feedback mechanisms also occur, such as in the activation of phenolase by an agent which produces active phenolase plus an additional molecule of activator (Chapter 6).

Regulation between Cells

In a multicellular organism each cell influences its neighbours, and even others remote from it. Although something is known of the effects of such widespread interactions, especially in embryogenesis, little has been achieved in understanding the means by which they are accomplished. On the other hand, great progress has been made in characterizing and unravelling the mechanisms of action of the hormones, those specific agents produced by endocrine glands and carried in the haemolymph, which may control the metabolism of the whole animal or influence individual organs. In spite of these successes, the most spectacular of which have been in the field of insect morphogenesis, the reader will find that when it comes to explaining hormonal regulation in molecular terms airy speculation sadly outweighs solid fact.

The number of instances of metabolic regulation by hormones in insects is now impressively large, and it seems that the degree of internal integration and control achieved by this means is just as great in the insects as it is in mammals. Hormonal mechanisms, some of which involve the interplay of a number of different chemical agents, control growth and differentiation, cuticular tanning, development of the gonads, the rate of heart beat and of peristalisis of the gut, diuresis, the mobilization of energy reserves, the activity of the central nervous system, and many aspects of behaviour. There is every reason to believe that this list is not complete.

Some hormones produce their effects by relatively simple mechanisms. Catecholamines, for instance, presumably induce the mobilization of glycogen in insects, as in mammals, by activating the enzyme which converts adenylic acid to its cyclic coenzyme form (Chapter 3). The corpus cardiacum hormone which controls the rate of heart beat has a two-stage mode of action. It is believed to stimulate a decarboxylase which catalyses the production of a second hormone, an indolealkylamine, which travels through the haemolymph to the target organ. How the indolealkylamine exerts its effect is not known.

The mechanisms of action of the hormones which control morphogenesis are more mysterious, but some progress has been made in understanding them, and once they have been established in molecular terms they will probably turn out to be as simple as those mentioned above. An account of present knowledge of these mechanisms, preceded by a brief review of the physiological effects of the hormones which control growth and development, is the subject of the next section.

Hormones and development

The spectacular morphological change known as meta-morphosis has always titillated the imagination of biologists, and the discontinuous nature of insect growth has encouraged an experimental approach to morphogenesis which has yielded a great deal of accurate information on the hormonal control of the process.[63, 74, 76] The sequence of events known as moulting, which includes an increase in cell numbers by mitosis, the secretion of a new cuticle, and resorption of part of the old, followed by dehiscence of the remainder, is initiated by the secretion into the haemolymph by the cells of the prothoracic gland of a hormone known as ecdysone. The prothoracic glands are themselves stimulated to secrete by a hormone, known as the brain hormone, which emanates from neurosecretory cells in the brain. The brain hormone is believed to travel down the axons of the modified neurones in which it is produced, to accumulate in the corpora cardiaca, thus forming a neural endocrine system comparable with the pituitary system of vertebrates. During larval life the expression of the moulting hormone is modified by the endocrine secretion of the corpora allata, with the result that larval form is retained at each moult. At the end of larval life production of this ' juvenile hormone ' by the corpora allata ceases, and the next two moults initiated by ecdysone produce first a partial (in the pupa), and then a full expression of the adult form.[74] The corpora allata resume secretion in the adult, producing a hormone, which seems to be identical with the juvenile hormone, but the effect of which is now gonadotrophic.

Notwithstanding the difficulty of obtaining quantities of hormone sufficient for chemical analysis, great progress has been made toward identifying the three growth hormones. The results of this work have been mentioned in previous chapters. The juvenile hormone is believed to be a terpenoid related to or derived from farnesol; ecdysone is almost certainly a steroid, and the brain hormone may well be one also.[63]

With the onset of differentiation in the embryogenesis of a

multicellular organism it is evident that some influences are at work to modify the expression of the genetic information of the zygote which is replicated in every daughter cell. These environmental influences may work on the nucleus, permitting the transmission to the cytoplasm of one set of genetic instructions in the cells of one region, and of another set in a different region, or they may act in the cytoplasm, where the genetic instructions are read and carried out. Many cells retain the ability to ' dedifferentiate ', that is, to revert to a general rather than a specialized cellular morphology when their environment is changed. The cells of insects and other animals which exhibit the phenomenon of polymorphism are capable of assuming more than one differentiated form. Presumably the nuclei of these cells transmit different sets of instructions to the cytoplasm in different circumstances. The polymorphism exhibited by all insects except the Ametabola is apparently controlled by the juvenile hormone. In the presence of the hormone, the genes responsible for larval morphology exert their effects but those responsible for adult form are suppressed; in the absence of the hormone, the reverse is true. In hemimetabolous insects, in which metamorphosis is gradual, the morphology of a single tissue, such as the epidermis and its cuticular covering, may differ between one moult and the next. Perhaps the mitoses which are a normal part of the moulting sequence permit an interlude of relative dedifferentiation in the epidermal cells, after which the cells can start afresh with a new set of genetic instructions. In the Holometabola the adult is formed wholly, or to a major degree, by the multiplication, growth and differentiation of groups of cells, many in discrete structures known as imaginal discs, which remain embryonic and relatively undifferentiated throughout larval life. During the pupal period these cells grow in size and number, replacing the larval cells, which degenerate.

More is known about the metabolic effects of the moulting hormone, ecdysone, than about those of the juvenile hormone.[37] In *Calliphora*, ecdysone produces an increase in the concentration of the *o*-diphenol oxidase and its activator, and also induces the appearance of the dopa decarboxylase, thereby shifting tyrosine metabolism towards the production of precursors of the tanning quinones (Chapter 6). Moreover, there is evidence that these metabolic effects are initiated in the nucleus, rather than in the cytoplasm, since the earliest detectable effect of the injection of ecdysone into the larvae of a fly from which the prothoracic glands have been removed is a morphological change in the chromosomes.[36] The giant chromosomes of the salivary gland cells of flies have for a long time been favourite objects of study by morphologists interested in chromosome structure and by geneticists mapping the positions of genes. Now they are proving equally valuable as indicators of the nuclear effect of hormones. The effect of the injection of ecdysone on the salivary gland chromosomes is the production of 'puffs' at two different positions on the chromosomes. These chromosomal puffs represent regions in which the DNA strands are loosened and separated. They are known to be centres of rapid RNA synthesis, and are generally recognized as signs of gene activity. The size and duration of the two puffs, which appear within one hour of the injection of ecdysone, are directly dependent on hormone concentration. The two loci activated experimentally are the same as those which show signs of activity before the onset of the moult in normal insects, although in the natural moulting sequence one puff precedes the other by an interval of one to two days. If the primary effect of ecdysone is on the nucleus, then we can assume that it stimulates or unmasks the genes responsible for the synthesis of the enzymes mentioned above, and probably others that are called for at the time of moulting. Of course we should not lose sight of the possibility that the production of chromosomal puffs is only one of the consequences of the initiation of the sequence of events that culminates in ecdysis, and that the primary action of the hormone is elsewhere; but the hypothesis of direct nuclear activation is plausible and attractive.

It is debatable whether ecdysone is a true growth hormone, in the sense of an agent activating the whole process of increase in size and dry weight, or is more strictly a moulting hormone, periodically stimulating the production of a new cuticle. There is evidence that the brain hormone activates protein synthesis in general. Stimulation of the prothoracic glands may be only one of the effects of the brain hormone, and a mutual effect of brain hormone and ecdysone on peripheral tissues is possible. The secretion of the corpus allatum which controls gonad development is also said to activate protein synthesis in a general way in the adult insect, but experiments do not eliminate the possibility of a mutual effect with the brain hormone here either. It seems logical to suggest that the brain is the master nuclear activator throughout life, the other hormones exerting their modifying effects against its generalized action, but physiological evidence is far too contradictory to allow such a statement to be made with any confidence.

Very little can be said about possible mechanisms of nuclear activation. It is known that the DNA of the nucleus is bound to basic proteins called histones, and it is possible that activation of a gene involves the stripping away of a masking protein. Because of the diversity of protein structure, such a mechanism would allow for a great degree of specificity in the action of the un-masking agents. On the other hand, experimental evidence suggests that the ratio of the concentrations of sodium to potassium ions may determine whether genes are active or quiet in chironomid salivary gland chromosomes. By stepwise alteration of this ratio it is possible to induce a series of puffs in gene loci in a sequence which parallels the natural sequence in the period from late larval to middle pupal life. This suggests that ecdysone and the juvenile hormone may not act directly on the chromo-somes, but may exert their effects by altering the sodium/potassium ratio of the nucleus.

Diapause

The occurrence in insects of interruptions in the progress of growth and differentiation, the phenomenon known as diapause, has provided physiologists with another opportunity for an experimental attack on the problem of the hormonal control of morphogenesis. We have already considered the energy metabol-ism of diapausing insects (Chapter 1) and have concluded that similarities in mechanisms of energy production in diapausing eggs and diapausing pupae suggest that growth is blocked at similar stages of development of embryonic cells destined to become larval cells in the one case, and adult cells in the other. The hormonal control of diapause has been studied most thoroughly in cases of pupal diapause in members of the Lepi-doptera. Here diapause is initiated by an interruption to the secretion of brain hormone, which induces a secondary failure of the prothoracic glands. It can be terminated experimentally by the implantation of actively secreting brains or of prothoracic glands. Whether the brain hormone has any effect other than stimulation of the prothoracic glands is problematical; certainly ecdysone is needed to initiate the pupal-adult moult, and ecdysone alone can induce this change in pupal abdomens isolated from their anterior halves.[76] This suggests that ecdysone can act as a complete growth hormone in the termination of pupal diapause.

Diapause in eggs of the silkworm is predetermined by the action of a hormone which circulates in the haemolymph of the female moth.[22] This hormone, which is produced from the suboesophageal ganglion of the moth, acts on the developing oocytes during a certain restricted stage of maturation, fixing the pattern of their future development outside the body of the parent. Here again a direct effect of the hormone on the information content of the nucleus seems possible, but nothing is known of the mechanism of action.

Diapause in adult insects is also possible, and here it seems certain that the prothoracic gland is not involved, since this organ degenerates at the beginning of adult life. The brain hormone may be the sole agent controlling adult diapause, although it has been suggested that the growth hormone of the corpora allata also plays a part.

Natural stimuli to diapause vary, but one of the commonest is photoperiod. Of the diapause-breaking stimuli, by far the most important is chilling by winter cold. These stimuli are believed to be perceived through the nervous system and conveyed directly to the secretory cells of the brain. Some suggestions have been made about possible molecular mechanisms involved in the interruption and resumption of secretion by the brain cells. The rate of termination of diapause in the eggs of a cricket by artificial agents, such as urea or ammonia, has a negative temperature characteristic reminiscent of the temperature characteristic of the denaturation of proteins by urea.[33] Clearly, a reaction which proceeds faster as the temperature is lowered has the properties required of an agent to break winter diapause. The reaction could be, for instance, the denaturation of a protein inhibitor. Other work on the biochemistry of the brain of a diapausing moth pupa has suggested that the accumulation of acetylcholine may be the significant event encouraged by low temperature. We are still a long way from an understanding of the molecular events of metabolic control in diapause.

One feature of diapause metabolism seems to be constant: there is a virtual or complete cessation of all anabolic processes. Protein synthesis ceases, as though some general nuclear activator, which could be the brain hormone, were removed. In adult diapause some tissues actually degenerate. This is especially evident in muscle, where first the mitochondria and later the myofibrils break down. Presumably those tissues with the highest rate of protein turnover are the first to degenerate when maintenance stops. But the block in protein synthesis is not complete. Diapausing pupae can repair wounds, with a local restoration of protein synthesis and a return of energy metabolism to that characteristic of active tissues. Moreover, the inter-segmental muscles of such pupae are apparently immune to diapause; they remain active, have a normal cytochrome system, and presumably carry on normal maintenance synthesis. Thus some cells are apparently independent of the action of a general nuclear activator, and others can throw off their dependence, or be activated by other means. The nucleic acid machinery of protein synthesis is probably subject to a number of different control mechanisms, which may act at several sites.

Regulation between Individuals

The final area of metabolic control to be considered, the control of the metabolism of one individual by an agent produced by another member of the same species, is particularly well developed in insects. An account has already been given of the chemical nature and physiological effects of the pheromones, as these agents are called (Chapter 4). Little can be said about the mechanisms by which they work. Many of them obviously have a trigger effect, working through nervous pathways to release behaviour patterns. Others may have a direct effect on metabolism. The queen substance of the honeybee, for instance, seems to inhibit ovary development directly in worker bees. The caste pheromones of ants and termites have a physiological effect which is clearly comparable with that of the juvenile hormone: they encourage the release of one of the multiple forms of a polymorphic organism. The chemical nature of the caste pheromones is unknown, but the fact that the juvenile hormone and a number of pheromones are terpenoids suggests that this class of compound may have a special significance in the control of metabolism.

References

1. AGARWAL, H. C., BROOKES, V. J., CHELDELIN, V. H. and NEWBURGH, R. W. 1963. Formate oxidation by *Phormia regina* larvae. *Comp. Biochem. Physiol.* **8**: 153.
2. ANDERSEN, S. O. 1963. Characterization of a new type of cross-linkage in resilin, a rubber-like protein. *Biochim. Biophys. Acta,* **69**: 249.
3. ARIAS, R. O. and TERRIERE, L. C. 1962. The hydroxylation of naphthalene-1-C14 by house fly microsomes. *J. Econ. Entomol.* **55**: 925.
4. BEARD, R. L. 1963. Insect toxins and venoms. *Ann. Rev. Entomol.* **8**: 1.
5. BENSAM, A., KITAZUME, Y. and YČAS, M. 1963. Ribonucleic acid metabolism in the silk gland. *Exptl. Cell. Res.* **31**: 329.
6. BRENNER-HOLZACH, O. and LEUTHARDT, F. 1961. Untersuchung über die Biosynthese der Pterine bei *Drosophila melanogaster*. *Helv. Chim. Acta,* **44**: 1480.
7. BRICTEUX, S., FUKUDA, T., DEWANDRE, A. and FLORKIN, M. 1959. Contributions to silkworm biochemistry. VIII. Conversion of pyruvate into alanine, glycine and serine of silk fibroin. *Arch. intern. physiol. et biochim.* **67**: 545.
8. BROWN, A. W. A. 1960. Mechanisms of resistance against insecticides. *Ann. Rev. Entomol.* **5**: 301.
9. BURSELL, E. 1963. Aspects of the metabolism of amino acids in the tsetse fly, *Glossina* (Diptera). *J. Insect Physiol.* **9**: 439.
10. BUTENANDT, A. 1959. Wirkstoffe des Insektenreiches. *Naturwiss.* **15**: 461.
11. CANDY, D. J. and KILBY, B. A. 1962. Studies on chitin synthesis in the desert locust. *J. Exptl. Biol.* **39**: 129.
12. CHEFURKA, W. 1959. Glucose metabolism in insects. *Proc. 4th Intern. Cong. Biochem., Symposium 12, Biochemistry of Insects,* p. 115 (L. Levenbrook, ed.). Pergamon, London.
13. CHINO, H. 1960. Enzymic pathways in the formation of sorbitol and glycerol in the diapausing egg of the silkworm, *Bombyx mori*. I. On the polyol dehydrogenases. *J. Insect Physiol.* **5**: 1.
14. 1963. Respiratory enzyme system of the *Bombyx* silkworm egg in relation to the mechanism of the formation of sugar alcohols. *Arch. Biochem. Biophys.* **102**: 400.
15. CLAYTON, R. B. 1964. The utilization of sterols by insects. *J. Lipid. Res.* **5**: 3.

16. COCHRAN, D. G. 1963. Respiratory control in cockroach-muscle mitochondria. *Biochim. Biophys. Acta,* **78**: 393.

17. COHEN, C. F. and BARKER, R. J. 1963. Vitamin A content and spectral response of house flies reared on diets with and without a vitamin A source. *J. Cell. Comp. Physiol.* **62**: 43.

18. COLHOUN, E. H. 1963. The physiological significance of acetyl-choline in insects and observations upon other pharmacologically active substances. *Advances Insect Physiol.* **1**: 1.

19. DAVEY, K. G. 1963. The possible involvement of an amino acid decarboxylase in the stimulation of the pericardial cells by the corpus cardiacum. *J. Exptl. Biol.* **40**: 343.

20. FORREST, H. S. and NAWA, S. 1962. Structures of sepiapterin and isosepiapterin. *Nature,* **196**: 372.

21. FRAENKEL, G. and HSIAO, C. 1963. Tanning in the adult fly: A new function of neurosecretion in the brain. *Science,* **141**: 1057.

22. FUKUDA, S. 1962. Hormonal control of diapause in the silkworm. *Gen. Comp. Endocrinol. Suppl.* **1**: 337.

23. GILBY, A. R. 1965. Lipids and their metabolism in insects. *Ann. Rev. Entomol.* **10** (in press).

24. GILMOUR, D. 1961. *Biochemistry of Insects.* Academic Press, New York.

25. GILMOUR, D. and ROBINSON, P. M., 1964. Contraction in gly-cerinated myofibrils of an insect (Orthoptera, Acrididae). *J. Cell. Biol.* **21** : 385.

26. GOLDSMITH, T. H. and WARNER, L. T. 1964. Vitamin A in the vision of insects. *J. Gen. Physiol.* **47**: 433.

27. GOODWIN, T. W. 1952. *The Comparative Biochemistry of the Carotenoids.* Chapman and Hall, London.

28. HACKMAN, R. H. 1959. Biochemistry of the insect cuticle. *Proc. 4th Intern. Cong. Biochem., Symposium 12, Biochemistry of Insects,* p. 48 (L. Levenbook, ed.). Pergamon, London.

29. HACKMAN, R. H. and GOLDBERG, M. 1963. Phenolic compounds in the cockroach ootheca. *Biochim. Biophys. Acta,* **71**: 738.

30. HANSON, J. 1956. Studies on the cross-striation of the indirect flight myofibrils of the blowfly *Calliphora. J. Biophys. Biochem. Cytol.* **2**: 691.

31. ——— 1956. Elongation of cross-straited myofibrils. *Biochim. Biophys. Acta,* **20**: 289.

32. HARVEY, W. R. 1962. Metabolic aspects of insect diapause. *Ann. Rev. Entomol.* **7**: 57.

33. HOGAN, T. W. 1961. The action of urea on diapause in eggs of *Acheta commodus* (Walk.) (Orthoptera: Gryllidae). *Aust. J. Biol. Sci.* **14**: 419.

34. HOSODA, J., SHIGEMATSU, H., TAKESHITA, H., MIZUNO, S., TAKA-HASHI, H. and MARUO, B. 1963. Ribonucleic acid metabolism in the posterior silkgland of silkworm, *Bombyx mori,* during the fifth instar. *Biochim. Biophys. Acta,* **72**: 544.

35. JENSEN, M. and WEIS-FOGH, T. 1962. Biology and physics of locust flight. V. Strength and elasticity of locust cuticle. *Phil. Trans. Roy. Soc. (London)*, B. **245**: 137.
36. KARLSON, P. 1962. On the chemistry and mode of action of insect hormones. *Gen. Comp. Endocrinol. Suppl.* **1**: 1.
37. ———. 1963. Chemistry and biochemistry of insect hormones. *Angew. Chem. (Internat. Ed.)*, **2**: 175.
38. KARLSON, P. and BUTENANDT, A. 1959. Pheromones (ectohormones) in insects. *Ann. Rev. Entomol.* **4**: 39.
39. KEILIN, D. 1925. On cytochrome, a respiratory pigment, common to animals, yeast, and higher plants. *Proc. Roy. Soc. (London)*, B. **98**: 312.
40. KENDREW, J. C. 1954. Structure proteins I, *The Proteins* (H. Neurath and K. Bailey, eds.), Vol. II, Part B, p. 845. Academic Press, New York.
41. KILBY, B. A. 1963. The biochemistry of the insect fat body. *Advances Insect Physiol.* **1**: 111.
42. KOIDE, F. and SHIMURA, K. 1962. 3-Phosphoglyceric acid dehydrogenase from the silk gland. *J. Biochem. (Tokyo)*, **52**: 302.
43. KONDO, Y. 1962. The cystathionine pathway in the silkworm larva, *Bombyx mori. J. Biochem. (Tokyo)*, **51**: 188.
44. LEVENBOOK, L. and KUHN, J. 1962. Properties and distribution of glutamine synthetase in the southern armyworm, *Prodenia eridania. Biochim. Biophys. Acta*, **65**: 219.
45. MCELROY, W. D. and SELIGER, H. H. 1963. The chemistry of light emission. *Adv. Enzymol.* **25**: 119.
46. MARUYAMA, K. 1958. Biochemical approach to muscle function in insects. *Conference on the chemistry of muscular contraction*, 1957, *Tokyo*. p. 53. Igaku Shoin, Tokyo.
47. MATSUMURA, F. and BROWN, A. W. A. 1961. Biochemistry of malathion resistance in *Culex tarsalis. J. Econ. Entomol.* **54**: 1176.
48. MOORE, B. P. 1964. The chemistry of the nasutins. *Aust. J. Chem.* **17**: 901ff.
49. NAGAYAMA, H., MURAMATSU, M. and SHIMURA, K. 1958. Enzymic formation of aminomalonic acid from ketomalonic acid. *Nature*, **181**: 417.
50. NIEMIERKO, W. 1959. Some aspects of lipid metabolism in insects. *Proc. 4th Intern. Cong. Biochem. Symposium* 12, *Biochemistry of Insects*, p. 185 (L. Levenbook, ed.). Pergamon, London.
51. NISIZAWA, K., YAMAKUCHI, T., HANDA, N., MAEDA, M. and YAMAZAKI, H. 1963. Chemical nature of a uronic acid-containing polysaccharide in the peritrophic membrane of the silkworm. *J. Biochem. (Tokyo)*, **54**: 419.
52. O'BRIEN, R. D. 1960. *Toxic Phosphorus Esters*. Academic Press, New York.

53. PFLEIDERER, W. 1963. Pterorhodin, ein neues natürlische Schmetterlingspigment. *Z. Naturforsch.* **18b**: 420.

54. POWNING, R. F. and IRZYKIEWICZ, H. 1961. Keratinase in insects. *Verhandl.* XI. *Internat. Kong. Entomol. Wien,* 1960, **1**: 1.

55. 1963. A chitinase from the gut of the cockroach *Periplaneta americana. Nature,* **200**: 1128.

56. PRICE, G. M. 1963. The effects of anoxia on metabolism in the adult housefly, *Musca domestica. Biochem. J.* **86**: 372.

57. RAZET, P. 1961. *Recherches sur l'Uricolyse chez les Insectes.* Imprimerie Bretonne, Rennes.

58. ROCKSTEIN, M. 1957. Some aspects of intermediary metabolism of carbohydrates in insects. *Ann. Rev. Entomol.* **2**: 19.

59. ROTH, L. M. and EISNER, T. 1962. Chemical defences of arthropods. *Ann. Rev. Entomol.* **7**: 107.

60. SACKTOR, B. 1961. The role of mitochondria in respiratory metabolism of flight muscle. *Ann. Rev. Entomol.* **6**: 103.

61. 1959. A biochemical basis of flight muscle activity. *Proc. 4th Intern. Cong. Biochem., Symposium* 12, *Biochemistry of Insects,* p. 138 (L. Levenbook, ed.). Pergamon, London.

62. SCHILDKNECHT, H. and HOLOUBEK, K. 1961. Die Bombardierkäfer und ihre Explosionschemie. *Angew. Chem.* **73**: 1.

63. SCHNEIDERMAN, H. A. and GILBERT, L. I. 1964. Control of growth and development in insects. *Science,* **143**: 325.

64. SIMON, H., WEYGAND, F., WALTER, J., WACKER, H. and SCHMIDT, K. 1963. Zusammenhänge zwischen Purin- und Leucopterin-Biogenese in *Pieris brassicae,* L. *Z. Naturforsch.* **18b**: 757.

65. SMITH, J. N. 1962. Detoxication mechanisms. *Ann. Rev. Entomol.* **7**: 465.

66. SRINAVASAN, N. G., CORRIGAN, J. J. and MEISTER, A. 1962. D-Serine in the blood of the silkworm, *Bombyx mori,* and other Lepidoptera. *J. Biol. Chem.* **237**: PC 3844.

67. STEELE, J. E. 1963. The site of action of insect hyperglycaemic hormone. *Gen. Comp. Endocrinol.* **3**: 46.

68. TIETZ, A. 1962. Fat transport in the locust. *J. Lipid Res.* **3**: 421.

69. TREHERNE, J. E. 1962. The distribution and exchange of some ions and molecules in the central nervous system of *Periplaneta americana* L. *J. Exptl. Biol.* **39**: 193.

70. WATERHOUSE, D. F. 1957. Digestion in insects. *Ann. Rev. Entomol.* **2**: 1.

71. WEIS-FOGH, T. 1960. A rubber-like protein in insect cuticle. *J. Exptl. Biol.* **37**: 889.

72. WHITE, J. W., SUBERS, M. H. and SCHEPARTZ, A. I. 1963. The identification of inhibine, the antibacterial factor in honey, as hydrogen peroxide and its origin in a honey glucose-oxidase system. *Biochim. Biophys. Acta,* **73**: 57.

73. WHITEHEAD, D. L., BRUNET, P. C. J. and KENT, P. W. 1960. Specificity *in vitro* of a phenoloxidase system from *Periplaneta americana* (L.). *Nature*, **185**: 610.
74. WIGGLESWORTH, V. B. 1954. *The Physiology of Insect Metamorphosis.* University Press, Cambridge.
75.   1963. The juvenile hormone effects of farnesol and some related compounds: quantitative experiments. *J. Insect Physiol.* **9**: 105.
76. WILLIAMS, C. M. 1952. Physiology of insect diapause. IV. The brain and prothoracic glands as an endocrine system in the cecropia silkworm. *Biol. Bull.* **103**: 120.
77. WYATT, G. R. 1961. The biochemistry of insect haemolymph. *Ann. Rev. Entomol.* **6**: 75.
78. ZEBE, E. 1961. Vergleichende Physiologie des Energiestoffwechsels von Muskeln. *Erg. Biol.* **24**: 247.
79. ZIEGLER, I. 1961. Genetic aspects of ommochrome and pterin pigments. *Adv. Genet.* **10**: 349.
80.   1963. Reinigung des Tetrahydropterins aus Insektenaugen. *Biochim. Biophys. Acta*, **78**: 219.

Index